Key Stage 3
Developing Numeracy

MEASURES, SHAPE AND SPACE

ACTIVITIES FOR TEACHING NUMERACY

year

Hilary Koll and Steve Mills

A & C BLACK

Contents

Coordinates

Construction and loci

Measures and mensuration

Answers

Published 2004 by A & C Black Publishers Limited
37 Soho Square, London W1D 3QZ
www.acblack.com

ISBN 0-7136-6476-2

Copyright text © Hilary Koll and Steve Mills, 2004
Copyright illustrations © Brett Hudson, 2004
Copyright cover illustration © Paul Cemmick, 2004
Editors: Lynne Williamson and Marie Lister

The authors and publishers would like to thank David Chadwick, Corinne McCrum and Jane McNeill for their advice in producing this series of books.

A CIP catalogue record for this book is available from the British Library.

Printed in Great Britain by Caligraving Ltd, Thetford, Norfolk.

A & C Black uses paper produced with elemental chlorine-free pulp, harvested from managed sustainable forests.

Introduction

Key Stage 3 Developing Numeracy: Measures, Shape and Space is a series of photocopiable resources for Years 7, 8 and 9, designed to be used during maths lessons. The books focus on the Shape, Space and Measures strand of the Key Stage 3 National Strategy *Framework for teaching mathematics*.

Each book supports the teaching of mathematics by providing a series of activities that develop essential skills in numeracy. The activities aim to reinforce learning and develop the skills and understanding explored during whole-class teaching. Each task provides practice and consolidation of an objective contained in the framework document. On the whole the activities are designed for pupils to work on independently, either individually or in pairs, although occasionally some pupils may need support.

The activities in **Measures, Shape and Space Year 9** relate to the following topics:
* geometrical reasoning: lines, angles and shapes;
* transformations;
* coordinates;
* construction and loci;
* measures and mensuration.

How to use this book

Each double-page spread is based on a Year 9 objective. The spread has three main sections labelled A, B and C, and ends with a challenge (**Now try this!**). The work grows increasingly difficult from A through to C, and the 'Now try this!' challenge reinforces and extends pupils' learning. The activities provide the teacher with an opportunity to make informal assessments: for example, checking that pupils are developing mental strategies, have grasped the main teaching points, or whether they have any misunderstandings.

This double-page structure can be used in a variety of ways: for example, following whole-class teaching the pupils can begin to work through both sheets and will experience gradually more complex questions, or the teacher can choose the most appropriate starting points for each group in the class, with some pupils starting at A and others at B or C. This allows differentiation for mixed-ability groups. 'Now try this!' provides a greater challenge for more able pupils. It can involve 'Using and Applying' concepts and skills, and provides an opportunity for classroom discussion. Where appropriate, pupils can be asked to finish tasks for homework.

The instructions are presented clearly to enable the pupils to work independently. There are also opportunities for pupils to work in pairs and groups, to encourage discussion and co-operation. A calculator icon indicates the parts of the activities in which calculators should be used. Where there is no icon, the teacher or pupils may choose whether or not to use them. Brief notes are provided at the foot of each page to assist the pupil or classroom assistant, or parent if the sheets are used for homework. Remind the pupils to read these before beginning the activity.

In some cases, the pupils will need to record their workings on a separate piece of paper, and it is suggested that these workings are handed in with the activity sheets. The pupils will also need to record their answers to some of the 'Now try this!' challenges on another piece of paper.

Organisation

Very little equipment is needed, other than rulers, sharp pencils, protractors, pairs of compasses and calculators. The pupils will also need squared paper, graph paper, thin card, tracing paper and scissors for some of the activities.

To help teachers select appropriate learning experiences for pupils, the activities are grouped into sections within the book to match the objectives in the Key Stage 3 National Strategy *Yearly teaching programmes*. However, the activities do not have to be used in the order given. The sheets are intended to support, rather than direct, the teacher's planning.

Some activities can be made easier or more challenging by masking or substituting some of the numbers. You may wish to re-use some pages by copying them onto card and laminating them, or by enlarging them onto A3 paper. They could also be made into OHTs for whole-class use.

Teachers' notes

Further brief notes, containing specific instructions or points to be raised during the first part of the lesson, are provided for particular sheets (see pages 6–7).

Whole-class oral and mental starters

The following activities provide some practical ideas to support the main teaching part of the lesson, and can be carried out before pupils use the activity sheets.

Geometrical reasoning: lines, angles and shapes

Tick-it!

On the board, draw a range of intersecting and parallel lines. Mark one or two angles with ticks, for example:

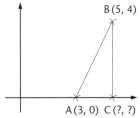

Invite pupils to come to the board and put more ticks on the diagram to show which angles can be determined using the angles already ticked. Discuss how each new angle can be worked out, and which angles, if any, cannot be determined.

Transformations

Use the scale

On the board, draw a simple plan of a room or town and label some lengths or distances. Choose an appropriate scale: for example, 15 cm to 1 m or 20 cm to 1 km. Ask the pupils to state the real-life distances between items or places on your plan (for instance, between the edge of the bookcase and the door, or between the hospital and the school). Then change the scale and ask the questions again.

Coordinates

Pythagoras' theorem

Draw a coordinate grid on the board and plot two points A and B, for example (3, 0) and (5, 4). Choose two pairs of coordinates where the *x*-coordinates are both even (or zero) or both odd, and where the *y*-coordinates are both even (or zero) or both odd. Then draw a right-angled triangle with the line AB as the hypotenuse, for example:

B (5, 4)

A (3, 0) C (?, ?)

Ask the pupils to give the coordinates of the other vertex, C. Then ask them to give the lengths of AC and BC (for example, AC = 2 units, BC = 4 units). Finally, ask the pupils to use their calculators and Pythagoras' theorem to find the length of the hypotenuse AB (for example, $2^2 + 4^2 = AB^2$).

Construction and loci

Town plan

Sketch a simple town plan on the board with several buildings or landmarks, showing perhaps a 2 km square. Include a Y-shaped road system or river and features such as a hospital, pond, fire station and school. Read out loci instructions and ask pupils to come to the front and mark where particular features or paths should be. Loci instructions could include:

An ambulance station is to be built at a point that is the same distance from the hospital as from the school.

A new road is to be built that travels exactly halfway between the two existing roads.

A path is to be made exactly $\frac{1}{2}$ km away from the pond.

Measures and mensuration

Circle sort

Copy the following columns onto the board. Explain that these are the radii, diameters, circumferences and areas of six circles, but that the measurements in each column are mixed up. Explain also that one number in one of the columns is incorrect. Tell the pupils that π has been taken as 3.14 and that numbers have been rounded to two decimal places.

Area	Radius	Diameter	Circumference
19.63	7	6	27.63
153.86	4.4	18	18.84
28.26	2.5	5	15.70
254.34	3	14	56.52
120.70	9	8.8	43.96
60.79	6.2	12.4	19.47

Ask the pupils to work out which measurements belong to the same circle (they may use calculators). The answers can be shown by drawing lines in the following way:

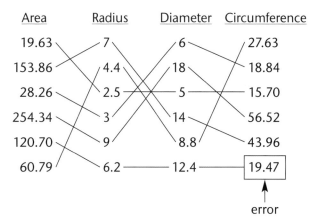

error

In a different lesson, give only the information in the area and circumference columns; ask the pupils to match the measurements in the same way.

Teachers' notes
Geometric reasoning: lines, angles and shapes

Pages 8 & 9

Begin the lesson by discussing the meaning of and differences between mathematical conventions, definitions and derived properties. Ensure the pupils realise that conventions are an agreed way of illustrating, notating or describing a situation, such as using arrows to show parallel lines or drawing a square corner to represent a right angle. A definition is a minimum set of conditions needed to specify a mathematical term: for example, the definition of a rhombus is *a quadrilateral with four equal sides*. Explain that a rhombus has other derived properties (non-essential information), but that the definition contains all the information that is required to identify a rhombus.

Pages 10 & 11

Ensure the pupils realise that the sum of an interior angle and its corresponding exterior angle is 180°, as the angles lie along a straight line. This activity leads the pupils to understand that the exterior angles of any polygon add up to 360°. This is demonstrated in part C, where a pencil is moved along the perimeter of a shape and is turned through each of the exterior angles. The pencil goes through one complete rotation.

Pages 12 & 13

This activity focuses on the sum of the interior angles of polygons. The pupils will notice that the interior angles of any quadrilateral total 360°, those inside any pentagon total 540°, those inside a hexagon total 720°, and so on. In part C, the pupils investigate the relationship between the number of interior triangles that can be drawn from one vertex of a shape, and the shape itself. The number of triangles, along with the idea that the interior angles of a triangle total 180°, enables the pupils to find the sum of the interior angles.

Pages 14 & 15

Revise angle rules, including those for corresponding and alternate angles, by drawing a pair of parallel lines and an intersecting line on the board, and asking the pupils to look for F and Z shapes in any orientation. After completing question C2, the pupils could be given other diagrams and asked to state which angles can be identified, given other sets of known angles.

Pages 16 & 17

For part C, the pupils will need small pieces of tracing paper (or acetate and an appropriate pen).

Pages 18 & 19

This activity introduces Pythagoras' theorem by demonstrating the link between the small squares on the sides of a right-angled triangle and the larger square on the hypotenuse. It is more important at this stage for the pupils to think of the questions spatially rather than trying to formulate an algebraic rule. They will need squared paper for part B.

Pages 20 & 21

This activity helps the pupils to appreciate that, if a shape is congruent to another, the length of each corresponding side and the size of each corresponding angle must be the same. The orientation of the shapes is not important. Explain that two shapes with equal corresponding angles and sides of different lengths, but in the same ratio, are said to be similar.

Pages 22 & 23

Discuss the relevant circle vocabulary on these pages before the pupils begin. Suggest real-life contexts for the terms: for example, a slice of pizza is a sector and a spoke of a wheel is a radius.

Pages 24 & 25

The pupils will need pairs of compasses and protractors for this activity. Demonstrate how to find the area of any regular shape by splitting it into triangles through the centre of the shape, finding the area of one triangle and then multiplying.

Pages 26 & 27

Some pupils find it difficult to visualise the plans and elevations of 3-D shapes using only 2-D pictures. If necessary, provide plastic 3-D shapes so that the pupils can examine the plans and elevations. Alternatively, encourage the pupils to draw nets and construct the shapes. They will need scissors and thin card for question C2.

Pages 28 & 29

This activity requires the pupils to visualise the cutting of 3-D shapes. As this visualisation can prove difficult for some pupils, it will be helpful to model these ideas practically: for example, using 3-D mathematical apparatus, or simply plasticine shapes and a knife.

Transformations

Pages 30 & 31

The pupils may find it helpful to check their answers using tracing paper. Where possible, encourage them to perform similar activities on a computer, using appropriate transformation software.

Pages 32 & 33

Revise the notation for translations: for example, $(2, ^-3)$. Explain that this is not a pair of coordinates when referring to translations; it tells you how many across and up/down to move each vertex of the shape. Show that positive values mean moving to the right or up, and that negative values mean moving to the left or down. Therefore the translation $(2, ^-3)$ means moving 2 units to the right and 3 units down. Provide several translations in this form and ask the pupils to give each translation in words. Discuss that there can be more than one set of transformations to map one shape onto another: for example, you could ask pupils who have completed part C to suggest several ways to map H onto E.

Pages 36 & 37

Demonstrate how to enlarge a shape from a point. Draw lines from each vertex of the shape to the centre of enlargement and then measure each line. The lines should be extended to twice as long if the scale factor is 2, three times as long if the scale factor is 3, and so on. Stress that the enlarged shape should look the same, only larger. Ensure the pupils realise that for fractional scale factors, the image will be smaller than the original shape. The pupils will need squared paper for question C3.

Pages 38 & 39

Part C shows that when a shape is enlarged by a scale factor, the lengths of the sides are multiplied by that number and the area is increased by the scale factor squared. To reinforce this idea, draw a simple 1×1 square and ask the pupils to enlarge it by the scale factor 2. Then show that since the length and the width have doubled, the area is four times larger (2×2), which is the scale factor squared.

Pages 40 & 41

Before the pupils tackle this activity, revise simple problems based on scale drawings. Write a scale on the board, such as 8 cm : 1 km. Call out some measurements on a map and ask the pupils to give the distances in real life (for example, 20 cm represents 2.5 km, 32 cm represents 4 km). Then call out real-life distances and ask the pupils to say what length on the map would represent them (for example, 0.5 km is represented by 4 cm on the map).

Coordinates

Pages 42 & 43

For part C, the pupils will need to be familiar with Pythagoras' theorem. Revise how the hypotenuse of a right-angled triangle can be found, given the length of the two smaller sides (for example, using the formula $a^2 + b^2 = c^2$). Provide examples on the board to assist the pupils.

Construction and loci

Pages 44 & 45

The pupils will require detailed demonstrations of the skills outlined on these pages. The National Numeracy Strategy illustrates these techniques fully on pages 221 and 223. Explain that the correct use of a pair of compasses ensures a much more accurate construction of mid-points and perpendiculars. Emphasise that the ruler is used mainly for drawing straight lines.

Pages 46 & 47

For part C, you could use a computer simulation to help the pupils examine the paths of points on the shapes being rotated: for example, using cycloid simulations on websites such as:

www.cut-the-knot.org/Curriculum/Geometry/Cycloids.shtml

Measures and mensuration

Pages 50 & 51

For part C, the pupils will need to be familiar with Pythagoras' theorem. Revise how the hypotenuse of a right-angled triangle can be found, given the length of the two smaller sides (for example, using the formula $a^2 + b^2 = c^2$). Provide examples on the board to assist the pupils.

Pages 52 & 53

The 'Now try this!' challenge requires the pupils to find the circumference of each circle, and then to calculate a fraction of the circumference. To find the fraction, the pupils should divide the angle given by 360° (a complete turn). This can be simplified, for example $\frac{45}{360} = \frac{1}{8}$.

Pages 56 & 57

As a further activity, tell the pupils that 1 cm^3 of water is equivalent to 1 ml, and ask them to find the capacity of each of the prisms on these pages (assuming negligible thickness in the sides of the containers).

Shape rules

A Read this list of ⬚ conventions ⬚. Then use them to help you label the diagrams.

☆ Arrows are drawn on lines to show that they are parallel.

☆ Short perpendicular dashes are drawn on lines of equal length.

☆ Capital letters are used to mark vertices. Lower-case letters are used to mark angles.

Example:

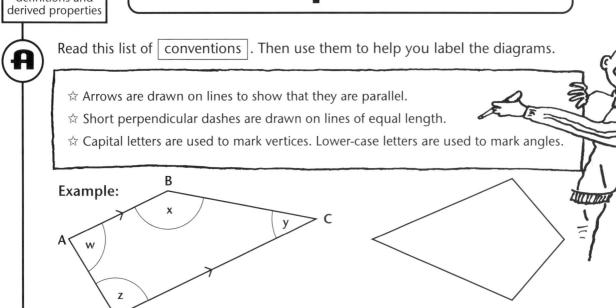

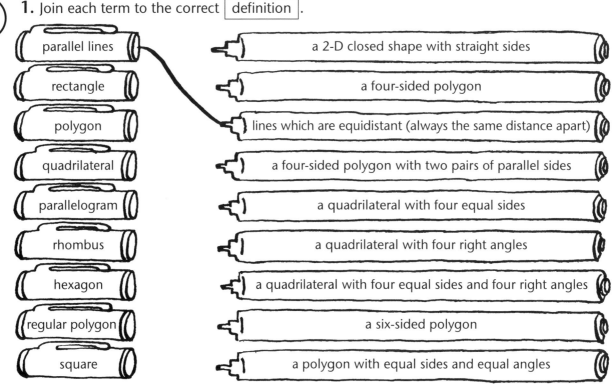

B 1. Join each term to the correct ⬚ definition ⬚.

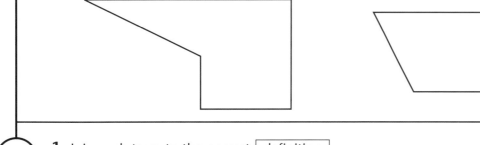

parallel lines	a 2-D closed shape with straight sides
rectangle	a four-sided polygon
polygon	lines which are equidistant (always the same distance apart)
quadrilateral	a four-sided polygon with two pairs of parallel sides
parallelogram	a quadrilateral with four equal sides
rhombus	a quadrilateral with four right angles
hexagon	a quadrilateral with four equal sides and four right angles
regular polygon	a six-sided polygon
square	a polygon with equal sides and equal angles

2. On the back of this sheet, write a definition for each of these terms. Work with a partner.

⬚ regular polygon ⬚   ⬚ perpendicular lines ⬚   ⬚ interior angles ⬚

 A **convention** is something that has been agreed as a way of recording or describing a mathematical situation. A **definition** contains the information that is *essential* in describing a mathematical term. The symbols on parallel lines look like this: ——→—— or ——≫——. The symbols on lines which are the same length look like this: ——┼—— or ——╫——.

Developing Numeracy
Measures, Shape and Space
Year 9
© A & C BLACK

Shape rules

C

This is a **definition** of a rectangle.

A rectangle is a polygon with four sides and four right angles.

There are other facts about a rectangle which are not essential to a definition. These are called | derived properties |. Here are some:

Its interior angles add up to 360°.

Its opposite sides are equal in length.

It has two pairs of parallel sides.

Write two derived properties for each definition.

(a) An equilateral triangle is a polygon with three sides of equal length.

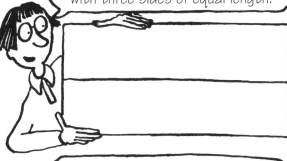

(b) A parallelogram is a polygon with two pairs of parallel sides.

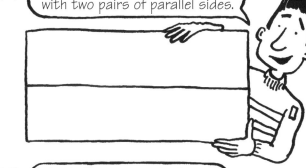

(c) A regular polygon is a polygon with equal sides and equal angles.

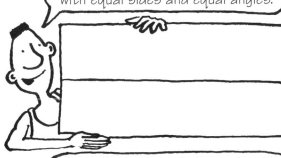

(d) Angle is an amount of turn and is measured in degrees °.

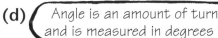

(e) The radius of a circle is any length from the centre to the edge.

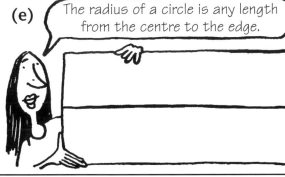

(f) A perpendicular line segment is one that is at right angles to another.

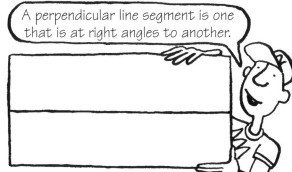

NOW TRY THIS!

• Write a definition for each of these terms. Give a derived property about the diagonals of each shape.

| kite | rhombus | isosceles trapezium | arrowhead (or delta) |

A **definition** contains the information that is *essential* in describing a mathematical term (for example, a square is a quadrilateral with equal sides and equal angles). **Derived properties** could be about symmetries, diagonals, sums of interior angles and so on. An **isosceles trapezium** is a trapezium in which the two opposite non-parallel sides are the same length.

Interior and exterior

A

1. The ⎡exterior⎤ angles of each polygon are labelled. Use these to find the **interior** angles.

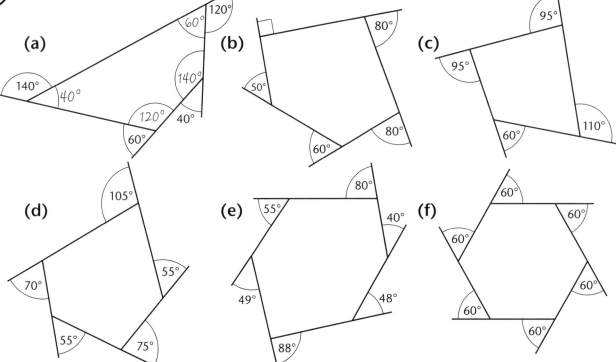

(a)   (b)   (c)

(d)   (e)   (f)

2. For each polygon above, find the sum of the **exterior** angles.

(a) _____   (b) _____   (c) _____   (d) _____   (e) _____   (f) _____

B

Label the missing exterior and interior angles of these shapes.

Use what you found out in question 2 above. **!**

(a)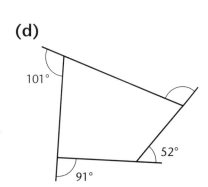

(b)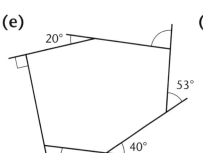

(c)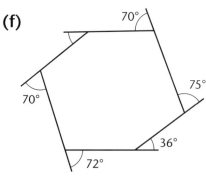

(d)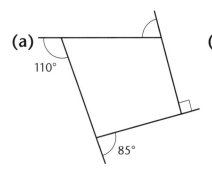

(e)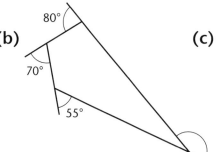

(f)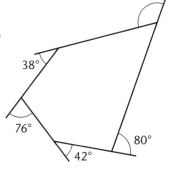

An **interior** angle is an angle inside a shape. An **exterior** angle is the angle formed when you extend one of the sides of the shape. Remember that an interior angle and its corresponding exterior angle lie along a straight line and therefore have a total of 180°.

Developing Numeracy
Measures, Shape and Space
Year 9
© A & C BLACK

Interior and exterior

C This diagram shows the path of a pencil which is placed along each side of a pentagon in turn. The diagram shows the angles the pencil turns through.

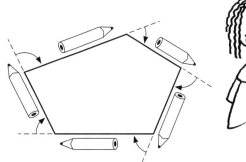

1. Explain to a partner why the sum of the **exterior** angles of any polygon is 360°. Use the diagram to help you.

2. The shapes below are **regular** polygons. Use the sum of the exterior angles of polygons to find the value of each exterior angle. Then find the interior angle.

(a)

Exterior angle =
360° ÷ 4 = 90°

Interior angle =
180° − 90° = 90°

(b)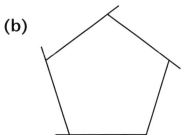

Exterior angle =
_____

Interior angle =
_____

(c)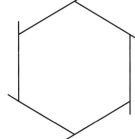

Exterior angle =
_____

Interior angle =
_____

(d)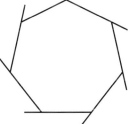

Exterior angle =
_____

Interior angle =
_____

(e)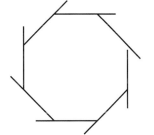

Exterior angle =
_____

Interior angle =
_____

(f)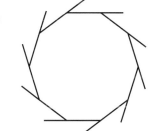

Exterior angle =
_____

Interior angle =
_____

3. How many sides has a regular polygon that has **exterior** angles of:

(a) 30° _____   **(b)** 24° _____   **(c)** 20° _____   **(d)** 10° _____

4. How many sides has a regular polygon that has **interior** angles of:

(a) 156° _____   **(b)** 150° _____   **(c)** 157.5° _____   **(d)** 162° _____

NOW TRY THIS!

- A regular polygon has *n* sides. Write a formula for finding the size of an interior angle of this shape, using the exterior angles.

Formula

An **interior** angle is an angle inside a shape. An **exterior** angle is the angle formed when you extend one of the sides of the shape. The exterior angles of any polygon add up to 360°. Remember, a **regular** polygon has equal sides and equal angles.

Interior designs

A Use the **exterior** angles of these polygons to help you find the **interior** angles. Then write the sum of the interior angles and the number of sides.

(a)

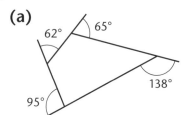

62° 65°
95°
138°

Sum of interior angles _____

Number of sides _____

(b)

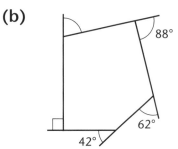

88°
62°
42°

Sum of interior angles _____

Number of sides _____

(c)

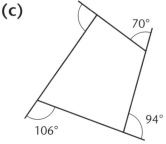

70°
106°
94°

Sum of interior angles _____

Number of sides _____

(d)

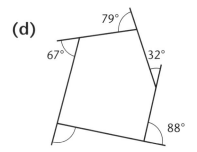

79°
67°
32°
88°

Sum of interior angles _____

Number of sides _____

(e)

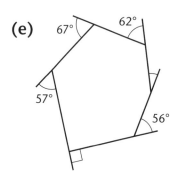

67° 62°
57°
56°

Sum of interior angles _____

Number of sides _____

(f)

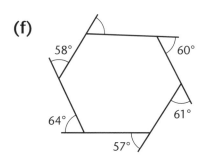

58° 60°
64° 61°
57°

Sum of interior angles _____

Number of sides _____

B Label the missing interior angles of these shapes. Use what you have noticed about the sum of the interior angles of quadrilaterals, pentagons and hexagons.

(a)

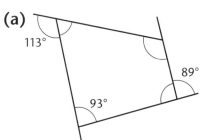

113°
89°
93°

(b)

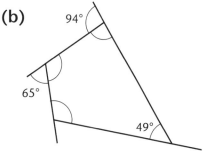

94°
65°
49°

(c)

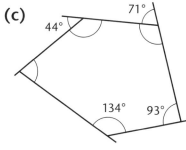

44° 71°
134° 93°

(d)

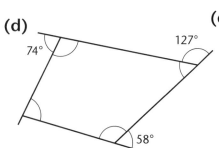

74° 127°
58°

(e)

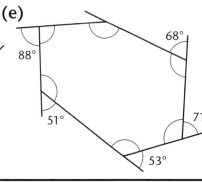

88° 68°
51°
71°
53°

(f)

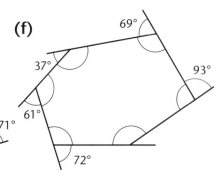

69°
37°
93°
61°
72°

An **interior** angle is an angle inside a shape. An **exterior** angle is the angle formed when you extend one of the sides of the shape. Remember that an interior angle and its corresponding exterior angle lie along a straight line and therefore have a total of 180°. The exterior angles of any polygon add up to 360°.

Developing Numeracy
Measures, Shape and Space
Year 9
© A & C BLACK

12

Interior designs

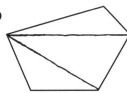

C

1. Split each polygon into triangles. To do this, draw straight lines from one vertex to each of the other vertices. Then complete the table to find the sum of the interior angles.

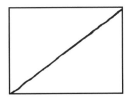 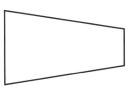 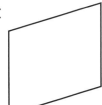

A B C D

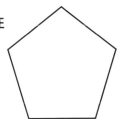 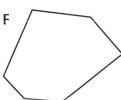 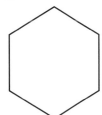 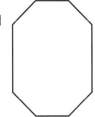

E F G H

Shape	Number of sides	Number of triangles	Number of triangles × 180°	Sum of interior angles
A	4	2	2 × 180°	360°
B				
C				
D	5	3		
E				
F				
G				
H				
–	n			

2. Write an equation to show the general rule for finding the sum of the interior angles of a polygon with n sides. _____

3. Complete the table below for polygons P, Q, R and S. Divide the sum of the interior angles by 180° to find the number of triangles. Then add 2 to find the number of sides.

Shape	Number of sides	Number of triangles	Number of triangles × 180°	Sum of interior angles
P			___ × 180°	1620°
Q			___ × 180°	2160°
R			___ × 180°	1980°
S			___ × 180°	4680°

NOW TRY THIS!

Let n be the number of sides of a regular polygon. Each interior angle in this polygon is 162°.

• Find the value of n. Use your equation from question C2.

$$(n - 2) \times 180 = 162n$$

 When you split a shape into triangles, make sure that all the lines you draw come from only one vertex. You multiply the number of triangles by 180° because the interior angles of each triangle total 180°. Look carefully for a pattern between the number of sides of a polygon and the number of triangles.

Angle appeal

A Find the value of each angle marked with a letter.

Look for **corresponding** and **alternate** angles. Extend lines to help you.

!

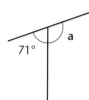 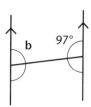 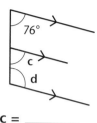 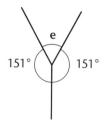

71° a

b 97°

76°
c
d

e
151° 151°

c = _____

a = _____   b = _____   d = _____   e = _____

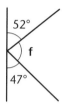 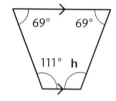 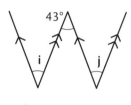

52°
f
47°

g
39°

69° 69°
111° h

43°
i   j

i = _____

f = _____   g = _____   h = _____   j = _____

 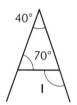 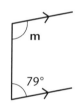 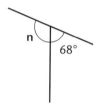 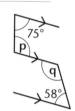

105°
k

40°
70°
l

m
79°

n
68°

75°
p
q
58°

p = _____

k = _____   l = _____   m = _____   n = _____   q = _____

B Find the value of each angle marked with a letter.

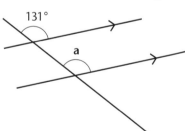 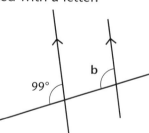 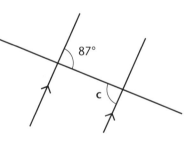

131°
a

99°   b

87°
c

a = _____   b = _____   c = _____

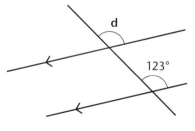 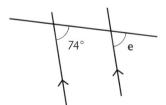 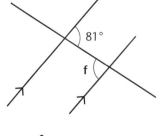

d
123°

74°   e

81°
f

d = _____   e = _____   f = _____

 When a straight line crosses two parallel lines, look for the equal angles in an 'F' shape. These are called **corresponding** angles. The equal angles in a 'Z' shape are called **alternate** angles.

Developing Numeracy
Measures, Shape and Space
Year 9
© A & C BLACK

C 1. Find the value of each angle marked with a letter.

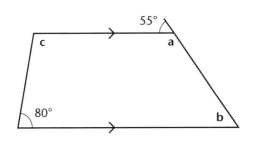

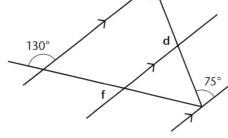

!

Extend
lines to
form
exterior
angles to
help you.

a = _____ b = _____ c = _____   d = _____ e = _____ f = _____

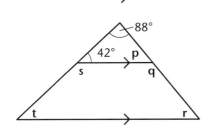

g = _____
h = _____
i = _____

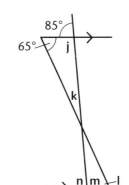

j = _____
k = _____
l = _____
m = _____
n = _____

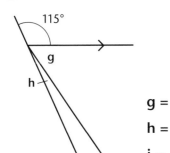

p = _____   q = _____   r = _____
s = _____   t = _____

2. If you know the size of the angles marked with a star, circle and triangle, which of the other angles can you find by calculating? Which cannot be found?

Discuss this with a partner and explain how you would calculate each angle.

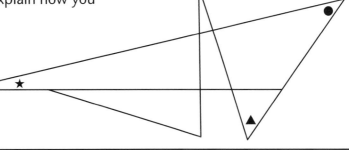

NOW TRY THIS!

- Draw a **parallelogram** and mark the exterior angles.
- Prove that each pair of adjacent interior angles of the parallelogram has a total of 180°. Use what you know about **corresponding** angles to help you.
- List other types of quadrilateral for which this is also true.

An **exterior** angle is the angle formed when you extend one of the sides of a shape. When a straight line crosses two parallel lines, look for the equal angles in an 'F' shape. These are called **corresponding** angles. The equal angles in a 'Z' shape are called **alternate** angles. Remember, a **parallelogram** has two pairs of parallel sides.

Where has my polygon?

A

1. Points A and B are two vertices of a triangle. The third vertex of the triangle lies on the dotted line.

   Measure positions of the third vertex to make the three different triangles below. Label the third vertex with the letter:

   ☆ C to make an **equilateral** triangle

   ☆ D to make a **right-angled** triangle

   ☆ E to make an obtuse-angled triangle.

2. What term can be used to describe any triangle where the third vertex lies on the dotted line? _____

3. Points P and Q are two vertices of a triangle. The third vertex of the triangle lies on the dotted line.

   Measure positions of the third vertex to make the three different triangles below. Label the third vertex with the letter:

   ☆ R to make a right-angled triangle

   ☆ S to make an **isosceles** triangle

   ☆ T to make an acute-angled triangle.

B

(a) Work with a partner. Describe fully the triangle that can be made when the third vertex is at these points.

> Describe angles as acute, right or obtuse. **!**

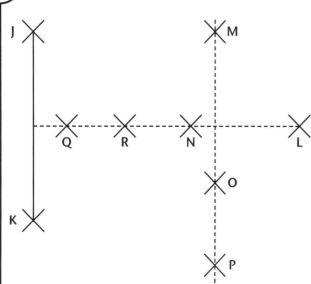

L	*acute-angled isosceles*
M	
N	
O	
P	
Q	
R	

(b) How many of the triangles are isosceles? _____

(c) Is it possible to draw a triangle with a reflex angle? Explain your answer. _____

_____

Remember, an **equilateral triangle** has three equal sides and three equal angles of 60°. An **isosceles triangle** has two equal sides and two equal angles. The sides and angles of a **scalene triangle** are all different. A **right-angled triangle** has one interior angle of 90°.

Developing Numeracy
Measures, Shape and Space
Year 9
© A & C BLACK

Where has my polygon?

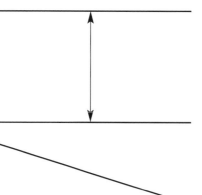

C

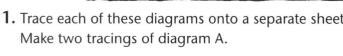
You will need five small sheets of tracing paper or acetate.

1. Trace each of these diagrams onto a separate sheet.
   Make two tracings of diagram A.

Diagram A

Diagram B

Diagram C

Diagram D

Lay one diagram over another and turn it. Describe the polygons that can be made when you turn:

(a) A over A	**(b)** A over B	**(c)** A over C
rhombus *square*		
(d) A over D	**(e)** B over C	**(f)** C over D

2. **(a)** Trace this pentagon. Draw two straight lines to split the shape into three parts. Then cut along the lines.

   Arrange the pieces to make different polygons. Sketch the polygons on the back of this sheet and name them.

   (b) Trace the pentagon again. Cut it into three pieces which can be arranged to make a square. Glue your square onto the back of this sheet.

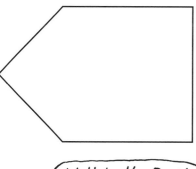

Well hello, Pretty Polly!

NOW TRY THIS!

- Draw a 4 × 6 rectangle and a 1 × 1 square.
- Cut the rectangle into four pieces using three straight lines. Arrange the pieces with the small square to make a larger square.

In the 'Now try this!' challenge, use the area of the original rectangle and square to work out what the area of the larger square will be. Once you know this, you can work out the length of each side.

Developing Numeracy Measures, Shape and Space Year 9 © A & C BLACK

17

Pythagoras problems

A 1. **(a)** Measure and label the sides and angles of these triangles. Write the lengths to the nearest millimetre. Check that the angles total 180°.

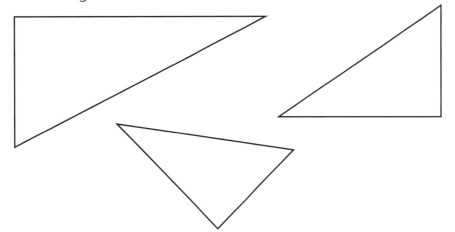

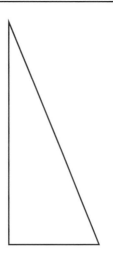

(b) What do all these triangles have in common? _____

(c) Which is the largest angle in each triangle? _____

2. Look at the smallest angle in each triangle. Describe its position in relation to the shortest side.

_____

B **(a)** Each of these **right-angled triangles** is surrounded by three squares. Find the area of each square by counting squares and half squares. Complete the chart.

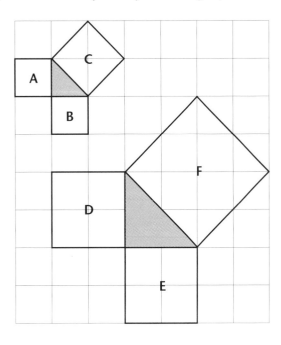

Square(s)	Area
A	1 cm²
B	
C	
A + B	
D	
E	
F	
D + E	

Ancient Mathematician at work.

(b) Write what you notice about the areas of the two small squares and the area of the larger square. _____

(c) Test your answer to question (b). Draw more diagrams on squared paper.

A **right-angled triangle** has one interior angle of 90°. The longest side of a right-angled triangle is called the **hypotenuse**. It is the side opposite the right angle.

Pythagoras problems

C

1. Find the area of the largest square in each diagram. Use what you have noticed about the areas of squares surrounding **right-angled triangles**.

(a)

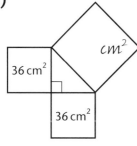

$36\,cm^2$ cm^2 $36\,cm^2$

(b)

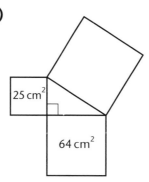

$25\,cm^2$ $64\,cm^2$

(c)

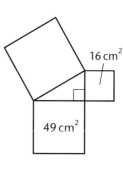

$16\,cm^2$ $49\,cm^2$

(d)

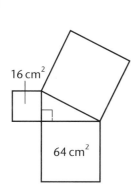

$16\,cm^2$ $64\,cm^2$

(e)

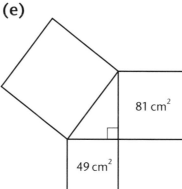

$81\,cm^2$ $49\,cm^2$

(f)

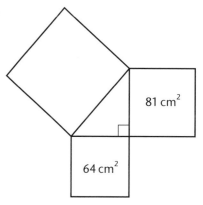

$81\,cm^2$ $64\,cm^2$

2. 🖩 Find the length of the | hypotenuse | of each triangle. Use the | √ | key on your calculator.

(a)

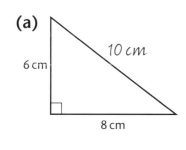

$6\,cm$ $10\,cm$ $8\,cm$

(b)

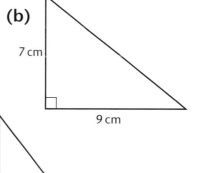

$7\,cm$ $9\,cm$

(c)

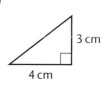

$3\,cm$ $4\,cm$

(d)

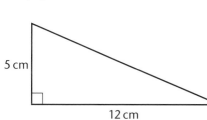

$5\,cm$ $12\,cm$

(e)

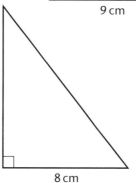

$10\,cm$ $8\,cm$

(f)

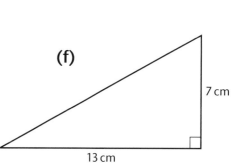

$7\,cm$ $13\,cm$

NOW TRY THIS!

• Tick the measurements which show the lengths of the sides of a right-angled triangle.

10 cm, 12 cm, 18 cm ☐   10 cm, 24 cm, 26 cm ☐   16 cm, 30 cm, 34 cm ☐

A **right-angled triangle** has one interior angle of 90°. The longest side of a right-angled triangle is called the **hypotenuse**. It is the side opposite the right angle. **Pythagoras' theorem** states: *In a right-angled triangle, the area of the square on the hypotenuse is equal to the sum of the squares on the other two sides.*

Congruent shapes

A Draw a | congruent | shape in each grid by rotating, reflecting or **translating** the first shape in the row.

B State whether each statement is true or false. Sketch examples to prove your answer.

(a) Two shapes that have identical corresponding angles must be congruent.

False. These have same angles but are not congruent.

(b) Two shapes that have identical corresponding angles and sides must be congruent.

(c) Two triangles with sides that measure 3 cm, 4 cm and 5 cm must be congruent.

(d) Two quadrilaterals with angles of 90°, 90°, 120° and 60° must be congruent.

(e) A parallelogram can always be split into two congruent triangles by cutting along the diagonal.

(f) Two triangles with two sides that measure 2 cm and 6 cm and one angle of 60° must be congruent.

Two shapes are **congruent** when they have the same shape and size, and corresponding sides and angles are equal. One shape may be a rotation, reflection or translation of the other. Remember, to **translate** a shape, slide it in a particular direction for a particular distance.

Developing Numeracy
Measures, Shape and Space
Year 9
© A & C BLACK

Congruent shapes

C Draw the diagonals of each quadrilateral. This makes four new shapes. Describe the shapes and say whether they are **congruent**.

Talk to a partner about how you can be sure of your answers.

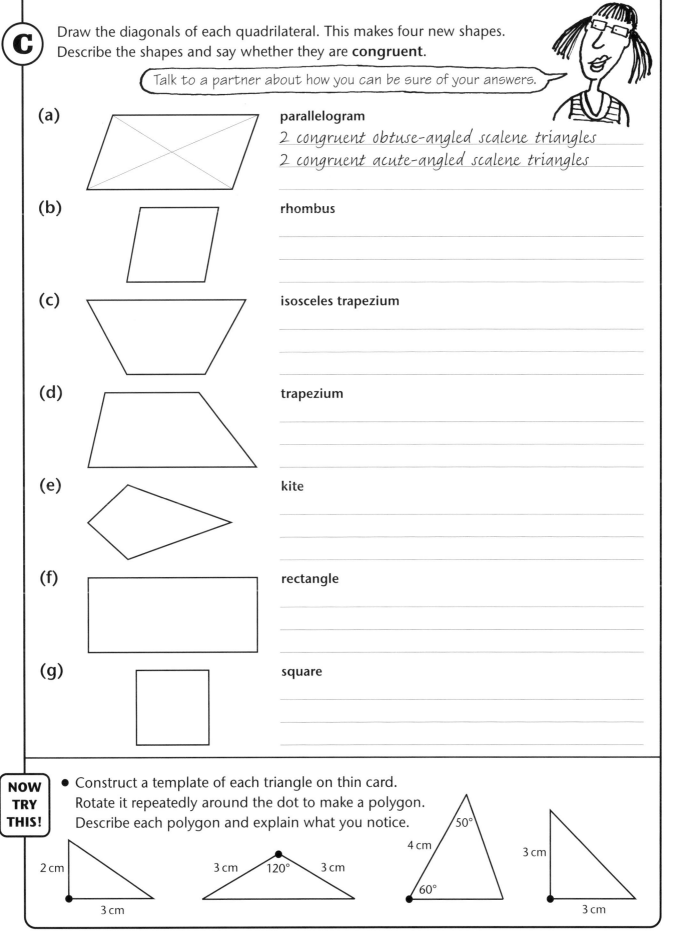

(a) parallelogram

2 congruent obtuse-angled scalene triangles

2 congruent acute-angled scalene triangles

(b) rhombus

(c) isosceles trapezium

(d) trapezium

(e) kite

(f) rectangle

(g) square

NOW TRY THIS!

- Construct a template of each triangle on thin card. Rotate it repeatedly around the dot to make a polygon. Describe each polygon and explain what you notice.

2 cm   3 cm

3 cm   120°   3 cm

50°   4 cm   60°

3 cm   3 cm

Two shapes are **congruent** when they have the same shape and size, and corresponding sides and angles are equal. One shape may be a rotation, reflection or translation of the other. In part C, if the shapes are not congruent, they may be **similar** or **different**. Similar shapes have equal corresponding angles, and the lengths of their sides are in the same ratio.

Round in circles

A Label the part of each diagram shaded or in bold. Choose from the words below.

Look up the words if you need to.

MATHS DICTIONARY

| circle | diameter | radius | circumference | arc | centre |
| chord | segment | tangent | semicircle | sector |

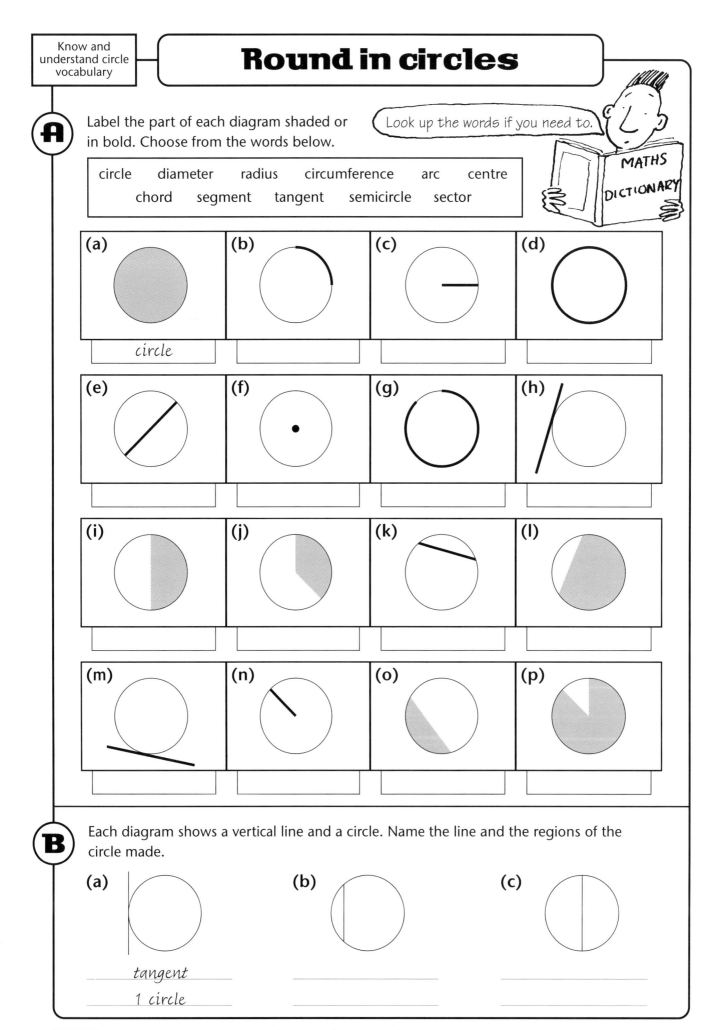

(a) circle

(b)

(c)

(d)

(e)

(f)

(g)

(h)

(i)

(j)

(k)

(l)

(m)

(n)

(o)

(p)

B Each diagram shows a vertical line and a circle. Name the line and the regions of the circle made.

(a) tangent
1 circle

(b)

(c)

 The definition of a circle is: *a circle is a set of points equidistant from its centre. Every radius of a circle is the same length.*

Developing Numeracy
Measures, Shape and Space
Year 9
© A & C BLACK

Round in circles

C 1. Follow the instructions. Draw straight or curved lines.

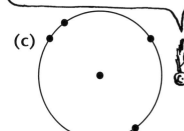
One has been done for you.

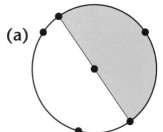
(a)

Join dots to show a diameter and half the circumference. Shade the semicircle.

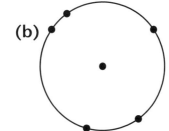
(b)

Join dots to show two radii and an arc. Shade the sector.

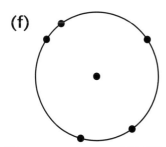
(c)

Join dots to show two radii and an arc that is greater than half the circumference. Shade the sector.

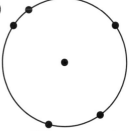
(d)

Join dots to show a chord and an arc less than half the circumference. Shade the segment.

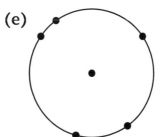
(e)

Join dots to show two radii and a chord. Shade the triangle.

(f)

Join dots to show two radii and two chords. Shade the quadrilateral.

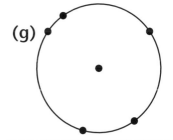
(g)

Join dots to show a diameter and two chords of different lengths. Shade the triangle.

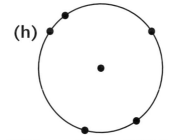
(h)

Join dots to show a diameter and two chords of equal length. Shade the triangle.

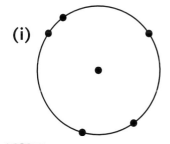
(i)

Join dots to show four chords. Shade the quadrilateral.

2. Describe each triangle or quadrilateral you drew in parts (e) to (i) above.

(e) _____   (f) _____

(g) _____   (h) _____

(i) _____

NOW TRY THIS!

- Draw a circle. Then draw two radii and two chords to make a kite.
- Draw a third radius to split the kite into two triangles.
- Describe the two triangles. _____

 In part C, use a coloured pencil to draw the lines, so that you can see the arcs you draw around the edges of the circles. The definition of a circle is: *a circle is a set of points equidistant from its centre.* Use a maths dictionary if you are unsure of any of the terms.

Circle investigation

A Each circle is split into equal sectors. Calculate the size of each angle at the centre.

(a)
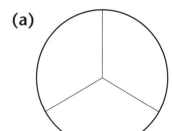

$360° ÷ 3 = 120°$

(b)
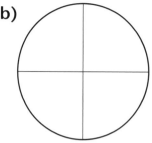

(c)
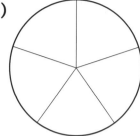

(d)
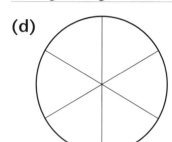

(e)
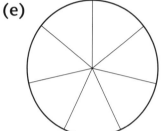

(f)
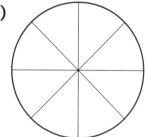

B Follow these instructions to investigate **regular** polygons drawn inside circles of the same size.

☆ Use a pair of compasses to draw six circles, each with a radius of 5 cm.

☆ Use a protractor to split each circle into a different number of equal sectors (3, 4, 5, 6, 7 and 8).

☆ Join the points on the circumference to form a regular polygon.

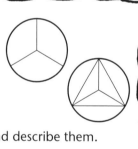

☆ Each polygon is made from a number of triangles. For each polygon, state the number of triangles and describe them.

(a) equilateral triangle	**(b)** square	**(c)** regular pentagon
Made from 3 isosceles triangles that have angles of 120°, 30° and 30°.		
(d) regular hexagon	**(e)** regular heptagon	**(f)** regular octagon

Remember, a **regular** polygon has equal sides and equal angles.
An **isosceles triangle** has two equal sides and two equal angles.
The sum of its angles is 180°.

**Developing Numeracy
Measures, Shape and Space
Year 9**
© A & C BLACK

Circle investigation

C 1. Follow these instructions to investigate areas of **regular** polygons drawn inside circles of the same size.

☆ Use a pair of compasses to draw six circles, each with a radius of 5 cm.

☆ Use a protractor to split each circle into a different number of equal sectors (3, 4, 5, 6, 7 and 8).

☆ Join the points on the circumference to form a regular polygon.

☆ Choose one of the triangles that makes up the polygon. Draw a **perpendicular** line from the centre of the circle to the base. Measure its length.

☆ Measure the base of this triangle and find its area.

☆ Now use this information to find the area of the regular polygon. Round your answers to 2 d.p.

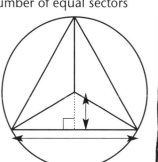

(a) Area of equilateral triangle	**(b)** Area of square

Area of isosceles triangle

$= \frac{1}{2} \times$ _____ $\times$ _____ $=$ _____ cm^2

Area of regular polygon

$=$ _____ $\times\ 3 =$ _____ cm^2

(c) Area of regular pentagon	**(d)** Area of regular hexagon

(e) Area of regular heptagon	**(f)** Area of regular octagon

2. Write what you notice about the areas of the regular polygons. _____

_____

NOW TRY THIS!

- Calculate the area of the circles you have drawn.
- Imagine that other regular polygons are drawn inside identical circles. Estimate the areas of the following polygons:

  (a) decagon **(b)** polygon with 25 sides **(c)** polygon with 100 sides

Use the formula $A = \pi r^2$. **!**

Remember, a **regular** polygon has equal sides and equal angles.
Perpendicular lines are at right angles to each other. To find the area of a triangle, use the formula $\frac{1}{2}$ base $\times$ perpendicular height. To find the area of a circle, use the formula $A = \pi r^2$, where A is the area and r is the radius of the circle.

A new dimension

A For each shape, sketch and name the | front and side elevations | and the | plan |.

(a)

Front

equilateral triangle

Side

rectangle

Plan

rectangle

(b)

(c)

(d)

B **1.** Join each description of a 3-D shape to the correct 2-D representation.

(a) The front and side elevations and the plan are all equilateral triangles.

(b) The front and side elevations and the plan are all circles.

(c) The front and side elevations are rectangles, and the plan is a square.

(d) The front elevation is a hexagon, and the side elevation and plan are rectangles.

(e) The front and side elevations are semicircles, and the plan is a circle.

(f) The front and side elevations are squares, and the plan is a larger square.

2. Is it possible to have a 3-D shape where the front and side elevations are squares and the plan is a rectangle? _____

The **front elevation** of a 3-D shape is the view you get when you look at it directly from the front. The **side elevation** is the view from the side (at 90° to the front). The **plan** is what you see when you look down on the shape from directly above.

**Developing Numeracy
Measures, Shape and Space
Year 9**
© A & C BLACK

A new dimension

C

1. The diagrams show the **front and side elevations** and the **plan** of some 3-D shapes. Sketch and name each 3-D shape. Then draw the net.

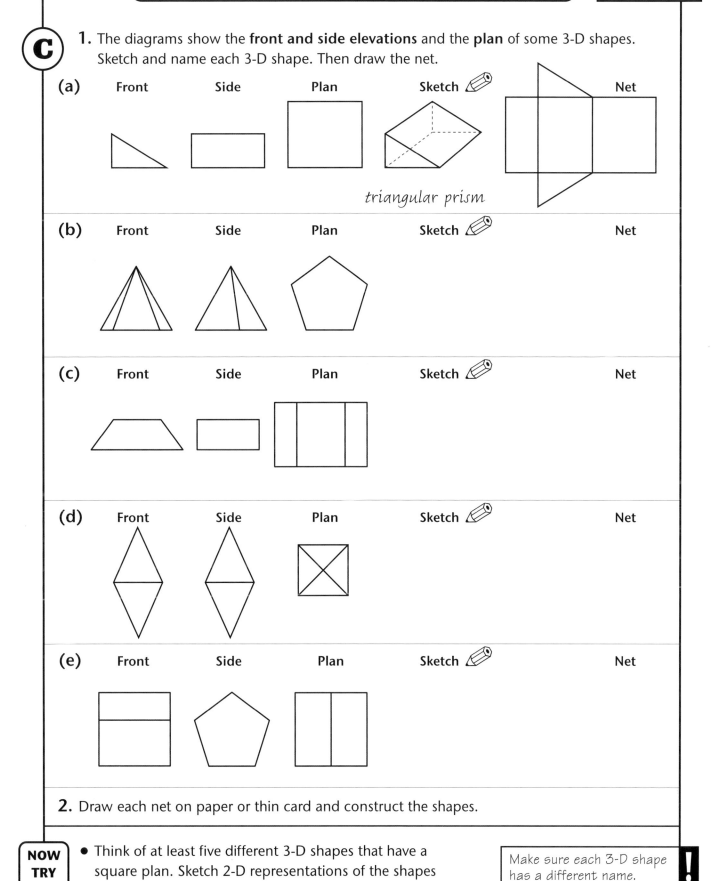

(a) Front   Side   Plan   Sketch ✏   Net

triangular prism

(b) Front   Side   Plan   Sketch ✏   Net

(c) Front   Side   Plan   Sketch ✏   Net

(d) Front   Side   Plan   Sketch ✏   Net

(e) Front   Side   Plan   Sketch ✏   Net

2. Draw each net on paper or thin card and construct the shapes.

NOW TRY THIS!

• Think of at least five different 3-D shapes that have a square plan. Sketch 2-D representations of the shapes and name them.

> Make sure each 3-D shape has a different name.

 The **front elevation** of a 3-D shape is the view you get when you look at it directly from the front. The **side elevation** is the view from the side (at 90° to the front). The **plan** is what you see when you look down on the shape from directly above.

Slice it

A 1. Each cube is sliced along the ⎡plane⎤ shown by the dotted line.
Name the shape of the ⎡cross-section⎤.

(a)   (b)   (c)   (d)

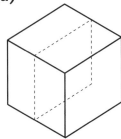 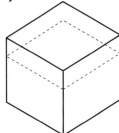 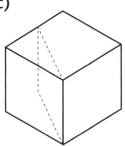 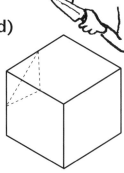

square _____ _____ _____

2. Each equilateral triangular prism is sliced along the plane shown by the dotted line.
Name the shape of the cross-section.

(a)   (b)   (c)   (d)

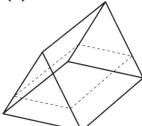 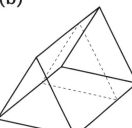 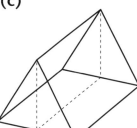 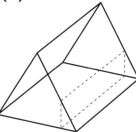

_____ _____ _____ _____

B 1. This square-based pyramid is sliced **horizontally**.

(a) Name the shape of the cross-section.

_____

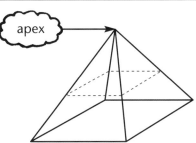

apex

(b) Describe the difference between cross-sections of a
horizontal slice made near the ⎡apex⎤ of the pyramid,
and a horizontal slice made nearer the base.

_____

2. Imagine that the same pyramid is sliced **vertically**.

(a) If the pyramid is sliced directly down through the apex, name the shape of the

cross-section. _____

(b) Describe the difference between cross-sections of a vertical slice made to one side

of the apex, and a vertical slice directly through the apex. _____

_____

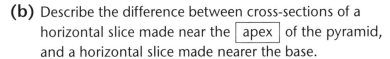
A **plane** is a flat surface which can be vertical, horizontal or sloping.
A **cross-section** is the face created by slicing a 3-D shape. The **apex** of a
square-based pyramid is the vertex that joins all of the triangular faces. If
the square base of the pyramid is placed on a table, the apex is at the top.

Slice it

Visualise sections obtained by slicing different planes

C

1. This cuboid is made from two cubes glued together.

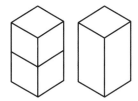

The cuboid is sliced along the **plane** shown by a dotted line. Name the two shapes that are made. If you do not know the name for a shape, write how many faces it has.

(a)

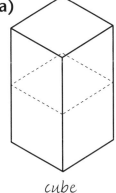

cube

cube

(b)

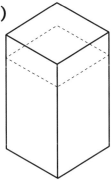

(c)

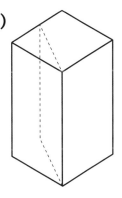

(d)

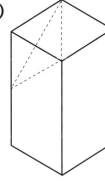

(e)

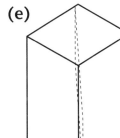

(f)

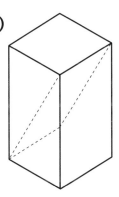

(g)

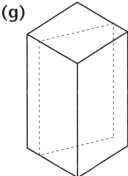

(h)

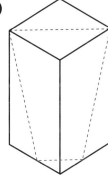

2. This cube is sliced along the plane shown to give a square **cross-section**.

Tick to show which of these cross-sections can be made by slicing a cube. Describe to a partner how they can be done.

rectangle ☐   non-square rhombus ☐   pentagon ☐

triangle ☐   regular hexagon ☐   trapezium ☐

NOW TRY THIS!

A ⌈ regular tetrahedron ⌉ is sliced along a plane to create a cross-section and two new shapes.

● Sketch some possibilities. Name the cross-section and describe the two shapes formed.

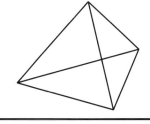

Example: Cross-section: triangle
Shapes: tetrahedron and a 5-faced shape

Do this as many times as you can. What do you notice?

 A **plane** is a flat surface which can be vertical, horizontal or sloping.
A **cross-section** is the face created by slicing a 3-D shape. Remember,
a **regular tetrahedron** has four identical faces. Each face is an
equilateral triangle (with three equal sides and three equal angles).

Developing Numeracy
Measures, Shape and Space
Year 9
© A & C BLACK

29

Move it!

A 1. Reflect each shape in the *x*-axis. The shapes will overlap and their outline will form a polygon. Name the polygon.

(a)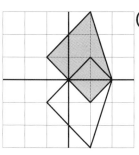

(b)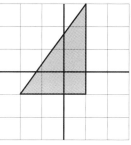

(c)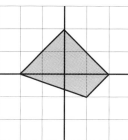

(d)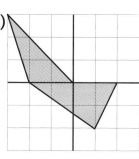

hexagon _____ _____ _____

2. Now reflect each shape in the *y*-axis. The shapes will overlap and their outline will form a polygon. Name the polygon.

(a)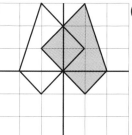

(b)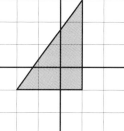

(c)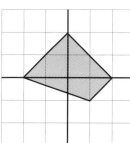

(d)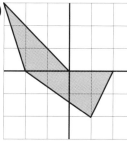

octagon _____ _____ _____

B 1. Reflect each shape in the *x*-axis, then reflect both shapes in the *y*-axis. The four shapes will overlap and their outline will form a polygon. Name the polygon.

(a)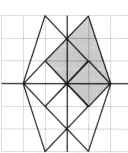

(b)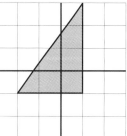

(c)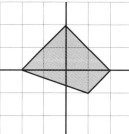

(d)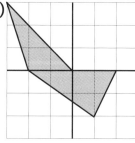

octagon _____ _____ _____

2. The patterns you have created are made from different polygons. Describe the polygons for each pattern.

(a) *4 right-angled triangles and 4 squares* _____

(b) _____

(c) _____

(d) _____

Remember, the *x*-axis is the horizontal axis and the *y*-axis is the vertical axis.

**Developing Numeracy
Measures, Shape and Space
Year 9**
© A & C BLACK

Move it!

C This trapezium has been rotated clockwise through 180° about the mid-point of one of its sides. The image and the original shape together form a regular hexagon.

1. Rotate each polygon clockwise through 180° about the mid-point marked. Name the shape formed by the original shape and its image.

(a)

parallelogram

(b)

(c)

(d)

(e)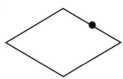

(f)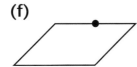

(g)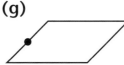

(h)

2. Each shape below is rotated clockwise through 180° about the mid-point marked. The shape formed by the original shape and its image is made into a tile. Sketch each tile on squared paper. State whether or not it will | tessellate | when it is **translated** repeatedly.

(a)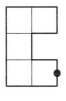

yes

(b)

(c)

(d)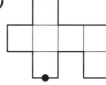

(e)

(f)

(g)

(h)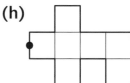

NOW TRY THIS!

- Draw a block capital letter on squared paper. Then rotate it clockwise through 180° about the mid-point of one of its sides.

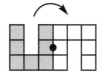

  Does the combined shape tessellate? _____

- Choose six block capitals from your name. Which letters produce a combined shape that tessellates? _____

  Try different mid-points. **!**

 When you rotate a shape, it may be useful to make a tracing of it. Then hold a pencil on the centre of rotation and turn the paper to check your image. A shape that **tessellates** can be rotated, reflected or translated to make a pattern which has no overlapping parts and no gaps between the shapes. To **translate** a shape, slide it in a particular direction for a particular distance.

Transformation tricks

A Write whether each statement is true or false.

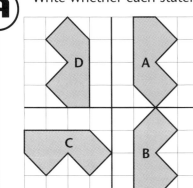

(a) B is a reflection of A   *true*

(b) C is a reflection of A   _____

(c) D is a rotation of B   _____

(d) C is a rotation of B   _____

(e) D is a rotation of A   _____

(f) C is a translation of A   _____

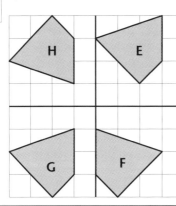

(g) E is a reflection of F   _____

(h) H is a rotation of E   _____

(i) H is a rotation of F   _____

(j) G is a rotation of E   _____

(k) G is a translation of E   _____

(l) G is a rotation of F   _____

B

1. Describe the single ⟨transformation⟩ that will map:

(a) D onto C

   A rotation clockwise about (2, ⁻5), through 90°.

(b) A onto F

_____

_____

(c) D onto B

_____

_____

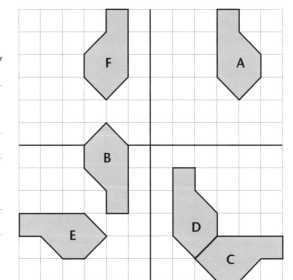

2. Two transformations can be used to map one shape onto another. Describe two transformations to map:

(a) F onto D   *The translation (0, ⁻7) followed by a reflection in the line*
     x = 0 (the y-axis).

(b) C onto F _____

_____

(c) E onto C _____

_____

A **transformation** can be a rotation, reflection or translation. To check reflections in a diagonal mirror line, it can be helpful to turn the paper so that the mirror line is vertical. Give translations using brackets: for example, (⁻5, 4) means moving the shape 5 units to the left and 4 units up. There are several possible pairs of transformations in question B2.

Developing Numeracy
Measures, Shape and Space
Year 9
© A & C BLACK

Transformation tricks

C

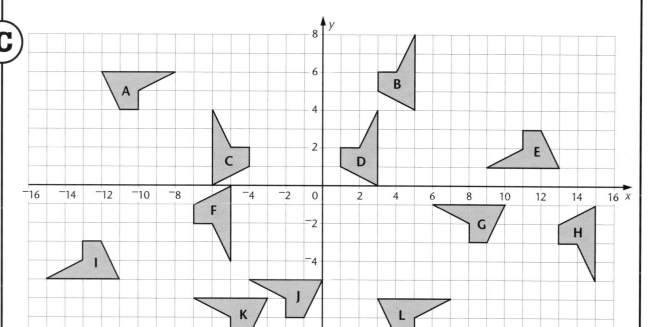

1. For each **transformation** below, write which shape maps onto another. All rotations are clockwise.

(a) Reflection in line $x = 0$ ___K onto L___

(b) Translation (2, 4) _____

(c) Reflection in line $y = x$ _____

(d) Translation ($^-$3, $^-$1) _____

(e) 90° rotation about ($^-$6, 6) _____

(f) Translation (24, 6) _____

(g) Translation ($^-$3, 1) followed by reflection in line $x = 0$ ___L onto J___

(h) Translation (3, 0) followed by reflection in line $y = 0$ _____

(i) Translation (3, 2) followed by 180° rotation about ($^-$4, 1) _____

(j) 270° rotation about (13, $^-$3) followed by reflection in line $x = 10.5$ _____

(k) 90° rotation about (9, 1) followed by translation ($^-$4, 7) followed by reflection in line $x = 5$ _____

2. Write transformations to map:

(a) H onto E _____

(b) J onto D _____

(c) K onto B _____

(d) L onto G _____

NOW TRY THIS!

A ┃commutative┃ transformation is one that returns the image to its original position when you perform the transformation twice.

● List the transformations above which are commutative.

A **transformation** can be a rotation, reflection or translation. To **translate** a shape, slide it in a particular direction for a particular distance. A **translation** describes the direction and distance in which the shape has slid: for example, ($^-$5, 4) means moving the shape 5 units to the left and 4 units up.

3-D symmetry

A

1. Different cuboids are made from 12 interlocking cubes. Each cuboid is then broken in half along a [plane of symmetry]. Which diagrams below correctly show a plane of symmetry?

A, _____

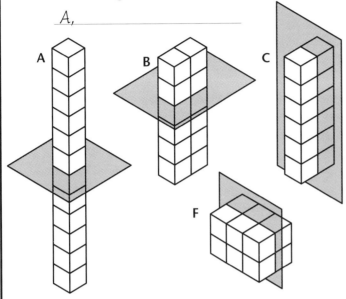

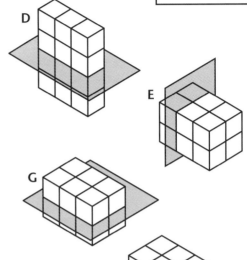

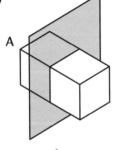

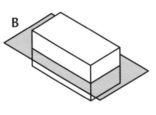

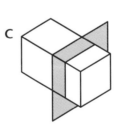

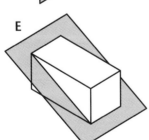

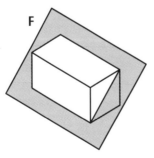

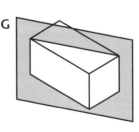

2. This cuboid is made from 16 interlocking cubes. Along how many different planes of symmetry can it be broken? _____

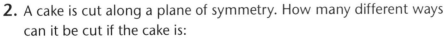

B

1. List the diagrams which correctly show a plane of symmetry. A, _____

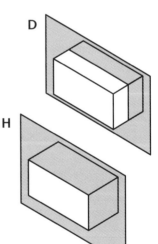

2. A cake is cut along a plane of symmetry. How many different ways can it be cut if the cake is:

(a) a cube? _____

(b) a regular hexagonal prism? _____

(c) a cylinder? _____

 Remember, a **plane** is a flat surface which can be vertical, horizontal or sloping. In a 3-D shape, a **plane of symmetry** is a plane which can act as a mirror to show the complete shape.

Developing Numeracy
Measures, Shape and Space
Year 9
© A & C BLACK

3-D symmetry

C Play this game with a partner. You need a counter each and one dice. You also need different-coloured pens.

☆ Take turns to roll the dice and move your counter. Move horizontally or vertically from square to square.

☆ Work out the number of **planes of symmetry** of the 3-D shape you land on. Write the number on the square and score that number of points. This shape cannot be used again.

☆ The winner is the first player to reach 20 points.

START

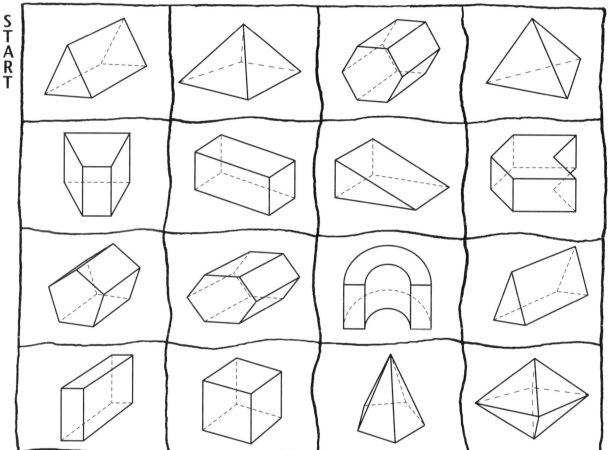

NOW TRY THIS!

● Explain how you can quickly calculate:

(a) the number of planes of symmetry of prisms _____

(b) the number of planes of symmetry of pyramids _____

● Use your answers to find the number of planes of symmetry of:

(c) a regular octagonal prism _____

(d) a regular decagon-based pyramid _____

In a 3-D shape, a **plane of symmetry** is a plane which can act as a mirror to show the complete shape. Check that the shapes on each side of the plane of symmetry are reflections of each other.

**Developing Numeracy
Measures, Shape and Space
Year 9
© A & C BLACK**

35

Little and large

A

1. Enlarge this shape by the
[scale factor] 2 from the point P.
Label the image A'B'C'D'.

2. Measure the length of side:

(a) AB _____   (b) A'B' _____

(c) BC _____   (d) B'C' _____

(e) CD _____   (f) C'D' _____

(g) DA _____   (h) D'A' _____

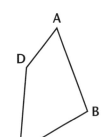

P •

3. Measure the angles in both shapes. What do you notice?

_____

4. Two shapes are [similar] when the sides are in the same ratio and
the corresponding angles are the same. Are these two shapes similar? _____

B

1. State whether the shapes in each pair are similar. If they are, give the
scale factor of the enlargement. The shapes are *not* drawn to scale.

(a)

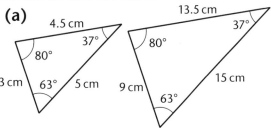

4.5 cm 37° 80° 3 cm 63° 5 cm

13.5 cm 37° 80° 9 cm 15 cm 63°

Corresponding angles are equal and

$\frac{9}{3} = \frac{13.5}{4.5} = \frac{15}{5}$ all equal 3

Shapes are similar. Scale factor = 3

(b)

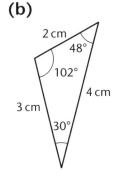

2 cm 48° 102° 3 cm 4 cm 30°

48° 3 cm 102° 6 cm 4.5 cm 30°

(c)

5.5 cm 11 cm 120° 130° 65° 16.5 cm

45° 3 cm 4 cm 130° 120° 65° 1 cm 2 cm 22 cm 45°

(d)

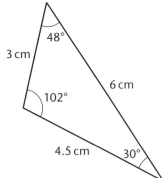

4 cm 58° 2.5 cm 146° 3.5 cm 66° 3 cm

10.2 cm 66° 146° 8.5 cm 58° 13.6 cm 11.9 cm

2. On the back of this sheet, draw and label at least three pairs of shapes, some pairs similar and
some not. Swap shapes with a partner. Find which are similar and give their scale factor.

The **scale factor** tells you what each length is multiplied by: for example,
if the scale factor is 4, a side of length 3 cm becomes a side of length
12 cm. In a pair of **similar** shapes, the ratio of any two corresponding sides
is equal to the scale factor, so A'B' ÷ AB gives you the scale factor.

Developing Numeracy
Measures, Shape and Space
Year 9
© A & C BLACK

Little and large

1. Enlarge this pentagon:

Label each image.

(a) by the **scale factor** 3 with the centre of enlargement at (0, 0)

(b) by the scale factor 2 with the centre of enlargement at (⁻3, 5)

(c) by the scale factor 5 with the centre of enlargement at (2, 3)

(d) by the scale factor 3 with the centre of enlargement at (4, ⁻1)

Measure the corresponding sides of the images to check your answers.

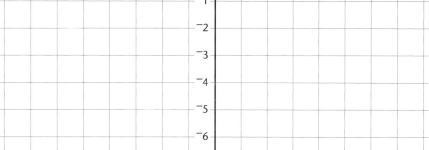

2. Enlarge this shape by the scale factor $\frac{1}{2}$ from the point P.

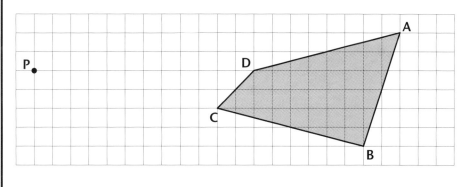

What do you notice about the image?

3. On squared paper, investigate enlargements of scale factors $\frac{1}{2}$, $\frac{1}{4}$ and $\frac{1}{3}$.

NOW TRY THIS!

- A triangle ABC has sides of 7 cm, 8 cm and 4 cm. It is enlarged by the scale factor 3. Find the perimeter of the image.

- Write an explanation of how to calculate the perimeter of an enlarged shape using the perimeter of the original shape and the scale factor.

The **scale factor** tells you what to multiply each length by: for example, if the scale factor is 4, a side of length 3 cm becomes a side of length 12 cm.

Looming large

A 7 mm
10 mm

B  14 mm
20 mm

C

D

F

E

Picture A has been enlarged. Measure and label the length and width of each picture. Give the **scale factor** (SF) for each of these enlargements.

(a) A enlarged to B *SF 2*   **(b)** A enlarged to C _____   **(c)** A enlarged to D _____

(d) A enlarged to E _____   **(e)** A enlarged to F _____   **(f)** B enlarged to C _____

(g) B enlarged to E _____   **(h)** B enlarged to F _____   **(i)** C enlarged to F _____

B

1. Calculate the perimeter of each picture.

Perimeter of A = *34 mm*   Perimeter of B = _____   Perimeter of C = _____

Perimeter of D = _____   Perimeter of E = _____   Perimeter of F = _____

2. 🖩 List the scale factors and find the ratio of the perimeters.

(a) A enlarged to B *SF 2*   Perimeter of B ÷ perimeter of A = _____

(b) A enlarged to C _____   Perimeter of C ÷ perimeter of A = _____

(c) A enlarged to D _____   Perimeter of D ÷ perimeter of A = _____

(d) A enlarged to E _____   Perimeter of E ÷ perimeter of A = _____

(e) A enlarged to F _____   Perimeter of F ÷ perimeter of A = _____

Use your answers to part A. **!**

3. What do you notice about the ratio of perimeters and the scale factors?

_____

 To find the **scale factor**, divide one length on the enlarged image by the corresponding length on the original shape.

Developing Numeracy
Measures, Shape and Space
Year 9
© A & C BLACK

Looming large

C

Here is rectangle A.

1. (a) Find the area of the rectangle.

_____ cm²

2 cm

3 cm   A

(b) Rectangle A is enlarged by the **scale factors** shown in the table below. Complete the table.

Enlarged rectangle	Scale factor	Length	Width	Area
B	2	6 cm	4 cm	24 cm²
C	3			
D	4			
E	5			
F	6			
G	7			

(c) Complete this table to compare each new area with the area of rectangle A.

Rectangle	Scale factor	How many times is area larger than area of A?
B	2	4
C	3	
D	4	
E	5	
F	6	
G	7	

(d) Describe what you notice. _____

_____

2. Find the area of the new shape if rectangle A is enlarged by the scale factor:

(a) 8 _____   **(b)** 10 _____   **(c)** 12 _____   **(d)** 20 _____

NOW TRY THIS!

• A square with sides 3 cm is enlarged by scale factor *x*. The area of the enlarged square is 225 cm².

  What is the scale factor? _____

• Make up three more puzzles like this for a partner to solve.

 When a shape is enlarged, the size of the angles remains the same. The lengths of the sides are multiplied by the **scale factor** and the area is multiplied by the scale factor squared.

On a smaller scale

A

Scales can be written in different ways.

1. Join equivalent scales with a line.

1 cm to 1 km	1 cm to 2 m	1 cm to 5 km	1 cm to 20 m

5 cm to 1 m	2 cm to 1 m	2 cm to 1 km

1 : 100 000	1 : 50	1 : 2000

1 : 20	1 : 200	1 : 500 000	1 : 50 000

(1 cm to 1 km is joined to 1 : 100 000)

2. Write each scale in a different way.

(a) 1 mm to 1 m → *1 : 1000*

(b) 2 mm to 1 m →

(c) 1 cm to 5 m →

(d) 2 cm to 5 m →

(e) 5 cm to 1 km →

(f) 1 cm to 10 km →

(g) 1 inch to 1 foot →

(h) 1 inch to 1 yard →

B

1. A map has the scale 1 : 2000 .

Write the scale in a different way. 1 cm to _____

Smallville Pop: Very Small

2. What do these lengths on the map represent in real life?

(a) 4 cm *80 m*   **(b)** 11 cm _____   **(c)** 18 cm _____

(d) 19 cm _____   **(e)** 25 cm _____   **(f)** 29 cm _____

3. How are these real-life lengths represented on the map?

(a) 10 m *0.5 cm*   **(b)** 40 m _____   **(c)** 100 m _____

(d) 70 m _____   **(e)** 230 m _____   **(f)** 1 km _____

 Remember, there are 12 inches in one foot and 3 feet in one yard.

**Developing Numeracy
Measures, Shape and Space
Year 9**
© A & C BLACK

On a smaller scale

C This diagram of a house is drawn using the scale $\boxed{1 : 150}$.

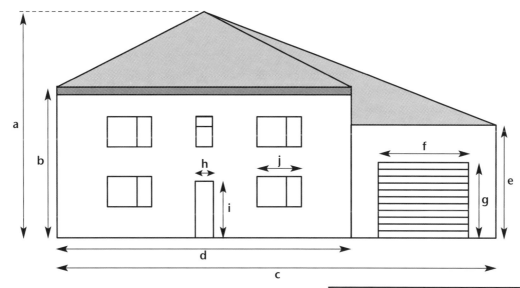

1. Measure the lengths on the diagram. Then work out the actual (real-life) measurements and complete the table.

2. Find the scaled area and the actual area of the garage door.

   Scaled area = _____

   Actual area = _____

   Is the actual area of the garage door 150 times larger than the scaled area? Explain your answer.

   _____

   _____

   _____

	Scaled length	Actual length
a	6 cm	
b		
c		
d		
e		
f		
g		
h		
i		
j		

 You need a sheet of graph paper.

NOW TRY THIS!

Make another scale drawing of the house and garage.
Use the actual lengths in the table and the scale $\boxed{2 \text{ cm to } 5 \text{ m}}$.
Write the scaled lengths here:

a = _____   b = _____   c = _____   d = _____   e = _____

f = _____   g = _____   h = _____   i = _____   j = _____

You could draw a table to help you with the measurements for scale drawings. Write pairs of measurements to show what lengths in real life are represented by lengths in the drawing (for example 1 cm : 0.2 m, 2 cm : 0.4 m, 3 cm : 0.6 m, and so on).

Developing Numeracy
Measures, Shape and Space
Year 9
© A & C BLACK

41

Understand
the nature of
triangles on a
coordinate grid

Coordinate clues

A 1. Plot each pair of points on the grid and join them with a line. This line is the **hypotenuse** of a **right-angled triangle**. Draw the other two sides of the triangle and label their lengths. Mark the mid-point of the hypotenuse and give its coordinates.

| A (0, 1) |
| B (4, 7) |
| Mid-point _____ |

| C (⁻6, ⁻1) |
| D (⁻8, 7) |
| Mid-point _____ |

| E (⁻1, ⁻2) |
| F (⁻5, 8) |
| Mid-point _____ |

| G (7, 6) |
| H (3, ⁻8) |
| Mid-point _____ |

| K (3, ⁻2) |
| L (⁻7, ⁻6) |
| Mid-point _____ |

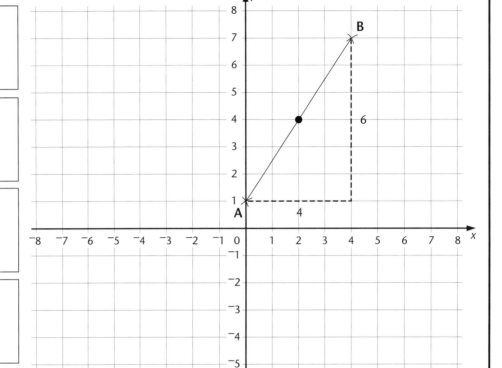

2. Read this formula for finding the coordinates of the mid-point of a line.

For the line segment AB joining $A(x_1, y_1)$ with $B(x_2, y_2)$:
- The x-coordinate of the mid-point is $\frac{1}{2}(x_1 + x_2)$
- The y-coordinate of the mid-point is $\frac{1}{2}(y_1 + y_2)$

Use the formula to check your answers to question 1.

B 1. Use the formula to find the coordinates of the mid-point (M) of the line PQ, if the coordinates of P and Q are:

(a) P (⁻6, 2) Q (5, ⁻4)   **(b)** P (⁻3, ⁻7) Q (5, 7)   **(c)** P (⁻5, 0) Q (4, ⁻6)

(d) P (⁻8, ⁻3) Q (0, 5)   **(e)** P (⁻8, ⁻6) Q (4, 4)   **(f)** P (⁻2, 7) Q (8, ⁻3)

(g) P (⁻1, ⁻4) Q (9, ⁻6)   **(h)** P (⁻5, ⁻2) Q (7, ⁻8)   **(i)** P (5, ⁻9) Q (⁻3, 5)

A **right-angled triangle** has one interior angle of 90°. The longest side of a right-angled triangle is called the **hypotenuse**. It is the side opposite the right angle. In part A, many different triangles are possible. One way to find the mid-point of a line is to count halfway from one x-coordinate to the other, and then repeat for the y-coordinates.

Developing Numeracy
Measures, Shape and Space
Year 9
© A & C BLACK

Coordinate clues

Understand
the nature of
triangles on a
coordinate grid

1. Plot each pair of points on the grid and join them with a line. This line is the **hypotenuse** of a **right-angled triangle**. Draw the other two sides of the triangle and label their lengths. Use **Pythagoras' theorem** to find the length of the hypotenuse to 1 d.p.

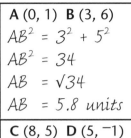

A (0, 1) **B** (3, 6)

$AB^2 = 3^2 + 5^2$
$AB^2 = 34$
$AB = \sqrt{34}$
$AB = 5.8$ units

C (8, 5) **D** (5, ‾1)

E (‾6, 7) **F** (‾1, 1)

G (‾7, ‾8) **H** (8, ‾3)

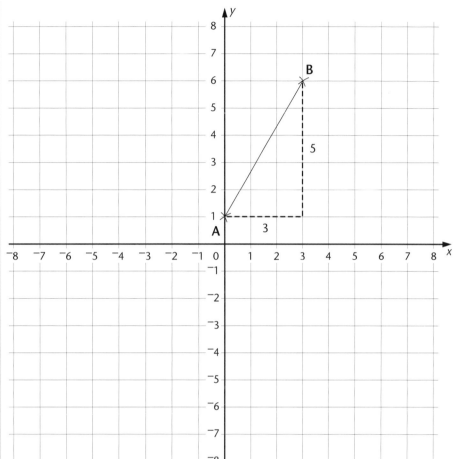

2. Play this game with a partner.

You each need a calculator.

☆ Each player chooses a pair of points from below.
☆ Calculate the distance between the two points. Record your answer to 1 d.p.
☆ The player with the smaller distance scores a point. The winner is the first to reach 4 points.

(4, ‾2) (9, ‾4) ____ units	(8, 1) (‾4, 6) ____ units	(8, ‾3) (‾4, ‾4) ____ units
(2, ‾8) (‾1, 2) ____ units	(3, ‾6) (6, 0) ____ units	(‾5, 7) (1, ‾2) ____ units
(5, 2) (8, ‾5) ____ units	(0, ‾5) (7, ‾1) ____ units	(‾8, 9) (‾7, 8) ____ units
(‾3, ‾1) (3, ‾7) ____ units	(‾7, 2) (‾3, 4) ____ units	(1, 5) (‾1, ‾1) ____ units

- Write a general rule to show the distance (d) between points A (x_1, y_1) and B (x_2, y_2).

_____

_____

The **hypotenuse** is the longest side of a **right-angled triangle**. It is the side opposite the right angle. **Pythagoras' theorem** states that the sum of the squares of the two smaller sides is equal to the square of the hypotenuse. In the game in question C2, think of the distance between the two points as the hypotenuse of a right-angled triangle.

Developing Numeracy
Measures, Shape and Space
Year 9
© A & C BLACK

Under construction

A Construct the **perpendicular** from the point P on each line. First use compasses to mark two points on the line equidistant from P. Then set the compasses to a larger radius. Draw two arcs from each of these points. Join the intersections of the arcs. One has been done for you.

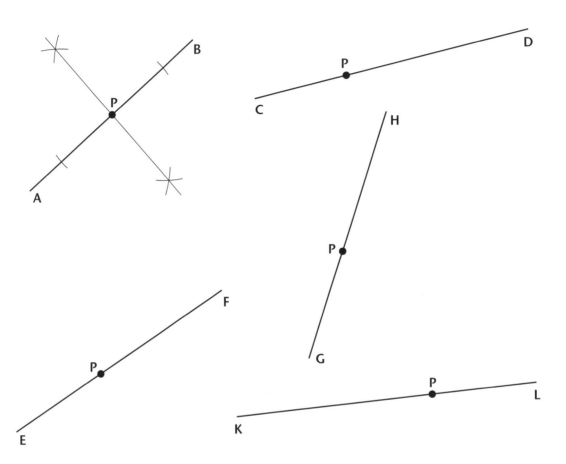

B 1. Construct these triangles on a separate sheet of paper. Use a pair of compasses and a ruler.

The triangles are not drawn to scale.

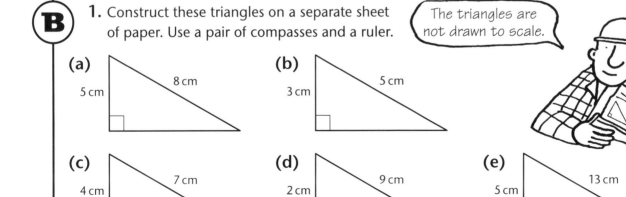

(a) 5 cm, 8 cm

(b) 3 cm, 5 cm

(c) 4 cm, 7 cm

(d) 2 cm, 9 cm

(e) 5 cm, 13 cm

2. Measure the length of the third side of each triangle.

(a) _____ (b) _____ (c) _____ (d) _____ (e) _____

 Perpendicular lines are at right angles to each other. For part B, first draw a horizontal line and construct a perpendicular to create the right angle. Measure and mark the length of the given vertical side. Then set your compasses to the length of the hypotenuse. Place the point at the top of the vertical line and draw an arc to cross the horizontal line.

Developing Numeracy
Measures, Shape and Space
Year 9
© A & C BLACK

44

Under construction

1. For each question, construct a triangle using the scale
    $1\ cm : 1\ m$. Put a tick next to the most accurate answer.

> Use a pair of compasses and a ruler.

(a) A 12 m ladder is leaning against a wall. The bottom of the ladder is 4 m from the wall. How far up the wall does the ladder reach?

11.3 m
10.6 m   11.8 m

(b) An 11 m ladder is leaning against a wall. The bottom of the ladder is 3 m from the wall. How far up the wall does the ladder reach?

9.7 m
10.3 m   10.6 m

(c) A 10 m ladder is leaning against a wall. The bottom of the ladder is 3 m from the wall. How far up the wall does the ladder reach?

9.1 m
9.5 m   8.9 m

(d) A 10 m ladder is leaning against a wall. The bottom of the ladder is 2.5 m from the wall. How far up the wall does the ladder reach?

9.7 m
9.1 m   9.9 m

(e) A 12 m ladder is leaning against a wall. The bottom of the ladder is 2 m from the wall. How far up the wall does the ladder reach?

11.3 m
10.9 m   11.8 m

(f) A 9 m ladder is leaning against a wall. The bottom of the ladder is 2.5 m from the wall. How far up the wall does the ladder reach?

8.9 m
8.6 m   7.9 m

(g) An 8 m ladder is leaning against a wall. The bottom of the ladder is 2.5 m from the wall. How far up the wall does the ladder reach?

11.3 m
7.6 m   7.3 m

(h) A 13 m ladder is leaning against a wall. The bottom of the ladder is 3.4 m from the wall. How far up the wall does the ladder reach?

12.5 m
12.2 m   11.9 m

2. Check your answers using **Pythagoras' theorem**.

NOW TRY THIS!

A ladder is unsafe if it leans at an angle of less than 73° to the horizontal.

- List the ladders above which are unsafe. Use a protractor to measure the angle between the base of each ladder and the ground.

When drawing and measuring, make sure you use a sharp pencil. To check your answers using **Pythagoras' theorem**, remember that the sum of the squares of the two smaller sides of a right-angled triangle is equal to the square of the hypotenuse. This can be written as $c^2 = a^2 + b^2$, where c is the hypotenuse.

Locus pocus

A **1.** Read each description carefully. Sketch the ⬚ locus ⬚ (the path of the moving object).

(a) A cat walks around a toy, always staying the same distance from it.

cat ○   toy ●

(b) A man is in a field with two bulls. He walks between them, keeping the same distance from one bull as from the other.

bull ●   bull ●

man ○

(c) A long thin bench is placed in a gymnasium. A girl walks around the bench, always keeping the same distance from it.

━━━━━━━━━

(d) A spider hangs on a thread and does not move. A midge flies around the spider, always keeping the same distance from it.

spider ●

2. Describe the shape of each path to a partner.

B **1.** Construct an accurate scale diagram of this situation. You need a pair of compasses and a ruler. Use the scale ⬚ 1 cm : 1 m ⬚.

A wall is 8 m long. A dog is tied halfway along the wall on a 3.5 m length of rope. Shade the area that the dog can reach. Name its shape.

Shape: _____

2. Calculate the area that the dog can reach. _____ m^2

A **locus** (plural **loci**) is the word used to describe a path traced out by a moving point. In maths, a locus is a set of points that satisfies a set of conditions. For part B, use the formula **Area of a circle** = πr^2, where r is the radius of the circle.

Developing Numeracy
Measures, Shape and Space
Year 9
© A & C BLACK

Locus pocus

C

1. Imagine that this square is being rolled along a straight line. Tick the diagram which correctly shows the path that point P would trace.

A

B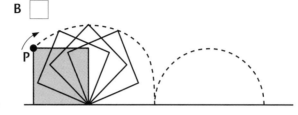

C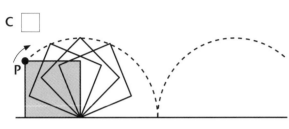

D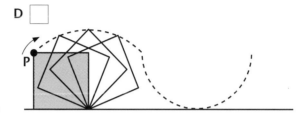

2. Imagine that this triangle is being rolled along a straight line. Tick the diagram which correctly shows the path that point P would trace.

A

B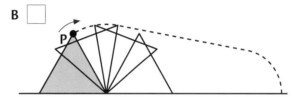

C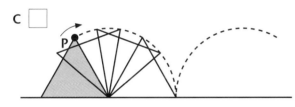

D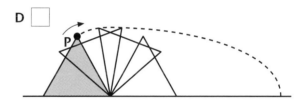

3. Imagine that a stick is glued flat onto each card, so that it lies in the same plane. The card and stick are held upright and spun very quickly. Join each card to the 3-D shape you would see.

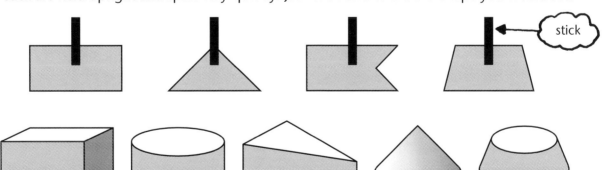

stick

NOW TRY THIS!

This is a 10-centimetre cube. A fly lands on the surface of the cube exactly 10 cm from vertex P.

● Describe all the positions in which the fly could be.

A **locus** (plural **loci**) is the word used to describe a path traced out by a moving point. In maths, a locus is a set of points that satisfies a set of conditions.

Developing Numeracy
Measures, Shape and Space
Year 9
© A & C BLACK

47

Measure for measure

A

One square centimetre has dimensions   1 cm × 1 cm

which is the same as   10 mm × 10 mm

So one square centimetre (1 cm²) is the same as 100 square millimetres (100 mm²).

A

One square centimetre has dimensions   1 cm × 1 cm

which is the same as   10 mm × 10 mm

So one square centimetre (1 cm²) is the same as 100 square millimetres (100 mm²).

1. How many square centimetres are the same as one square metre? Fill in the gaps below.

One square metre has dimensions   1 m × 1 m

which is the same as   _____ cm × _____ cm

So one square metre (1 m²) is the same as _____ square centimetres (_____ cm²).

2. Convert these measurements to the units shown.

(a) 5 cm² = _____ mm²

(b) 12 cm² = _____ mm²

(c) 50 000 mm² = _____ cm²

(d) 75 000 mm² = _____ cm²

(e) 6 m² = _____ cm²

(f) 15 m² = _____ cm²

(g) 65 000 cm² = _____ m²

(h) 150 000 cm² = _____ m²

3. One hectare (ha) equals 10 000 m². Convert these measurements to hectares.

(a) 50 000 m² = _____*ha*   **(b)** 125 000 m² = _____   **(c)** 5000 m² = _____

(d) 100 000 m² = _____   **(e)** 350 000 m² = _____   **(f)** 2500 m² = _____

B

One cubic centimetre has dimensions   1 cm × 1 cm × 1 cm

which is the same as   10 mm × 10 mm × 10 mm

So one cubic centimetre (1 cm³) is the same as 1000 cubic millimetres (1000 mm³).

1. How many cubic centimetres are the same as one cubic metre? Fill in the gaps below.

One cubic metre has dimensions   1 m × 1 m × 1 m

which is the same as   _____ cm × _____ cm × _____ cm

So one cubic metre (1 m³) is the same as _____ cubic centimetres (_____ cm³).

2. Convert these measurements to the units shown.

(a) 4 cm³ = _____ mm³

(b) 10 cm³ = _____ mm³

(c) 50 000 mm³ = _____ cm³

(d) 28 000 mm³ = _____ cm³

(e) 100 m³ = _____ cm³

(f) 1000 m³ = _____ cm³

(g) 2 000 000 cm³ = _____ m³

(h) 500 000 cm³ = _____ m³

Square metres, square centimetres and square millimetres are the metric units for measuring area and surface area. Cubic metres, cubic centimetres and cubic millimetres are the metric units for measuring volume (the amount of space something takes up).

Developing Numeracy
Measures, Shape and Space
Year 9
© A & C BLACK

Convert between area measures and between volume measures

C

1. Find the total area of the shaded shapes in each diagram.
   Work out the answer in square centimetres (cm²), then convert
   it to square millimetres (mm²).

(a)

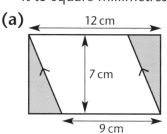

12 cm
7 cm
9 cm

(b)

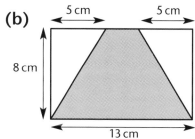

5 cm   5 cm
8 cm
13 cm

Use what you know about the areas of rectangles, triangles and parallelograms. **!**

_____ _mm²_

(c)

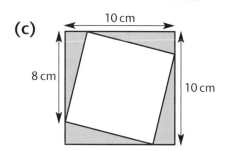

10 cm
8 cm
10 cm

(d)

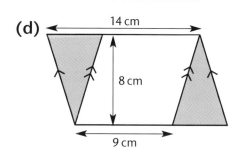

14 cm
8 cm
9 cm

2. Calculate the volume of each cuboid in cubic centimetres (cm³). Convert the answer to
   cubic millimetres (mm³).

(a)

7 cm
4 cm
5 cm

(b)

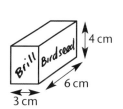

4 cm
6 cm
3 cm

(c)

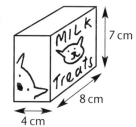

7 cm
8 cm
4 cm

_____ _mm³_

(d)

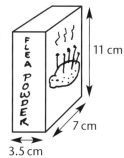

11 cm
7 cm
3.5 cm

(e)

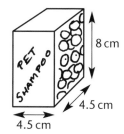

8 cm
4.5 cm
4.5 cm

(f)

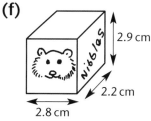

2.9 cm
2.2 cm
2.8 cm

NOW TRY THIS!

- Find the [surface area] of each cuboid in square centimetres (cm²).
  Convert the answer to square millimetres (mm²).

- To check your answers, convert the dimensions of each cuboid to
  millimetres, then find the surface area using these numbers.

Remember: 1 cm² is the same as 100 mm²; 1 cm³ is the same as 1000 mm³.
In part C, think about using subtraction: you could find the area of the
whole shape and then subtract the unshaded parts. To find the area of a
parallelogram, multiply the base by the perpendicular height. The **surface
area** of a 3-D shape is the amount of surface on all its faces added together.

Developing Numeracy
Measures, Shape and Space
Year 9
© A & C BLACK

49

Bearing up

Look at these diagrams and answer the questions.

1.

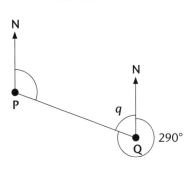

(a) What is the bearing of B from A?

_210°_

(b) What is the angle marked *a*?

(c) What is the bearing of A from B?

The two North lines are parallel, so the angles in the U shape total 180°.
$a + b = 180°$

2.

(a) What is the bearing of P from Q?

(b) What is the angle marked *q*?

(c) What is the bearing of Q from P?

3.

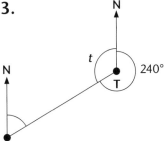

(a) What is the bearing of S from T?

(b) What is the angle marked *t*?

(c) What is the bearing of T from S?

4.

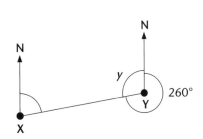

(a) What is the bearing of X from Y?

(b) What is the angle marked *y*?

(c) What is the bearing of Y from X?

B

1. Calculate these bearings using the information given. _You can draw a sketch to help._

(a) The bearing of C from D is 225°. What is the bearing of D from C? _____

(b) The bearing of E from F is 075°. What is the bearing of F from E? _____

(c) The bearing of G from H is 175°. What is the bearing of H from G? _____

(d) The bearing of K from L is 315°. What is the bearing of L from K? _____

(e) The bearing of M from N is 045°. What is the bearing of N from M? _____

(f) The bearing of P from Q is 137°. What is the bearing of Q from P? _____

2. Now check your answers. Draw accurate diagrams using a protractor.

A **bearing** should always contain three figures. For angles up to 100°, write a zero at the beginning (for example, 012°, 030°, 054°). To give a bearing, use the expression 'the bearing of (...) from (...) is...' The letter that follows the word 'from' is the point at which the angle is, so 'the bearing of B from A' is the clockwise angle at A. The arrow for North always points up the page.

Developing Numeracy
Measures, Shape and Space
Year 9
© A & C BLACK

Bearing up

C Follow these instructions carefully.

☆ Draw a line to show the direct route from the helipad to each boat in distress.

☆ Estimate the **bearing** of the boat from the pad. Then calculate its distance using **Pythagoras' theorem**. Each square represents 1 nautical mile.

☆ Complete each alert form for the helicopter rescue crew.

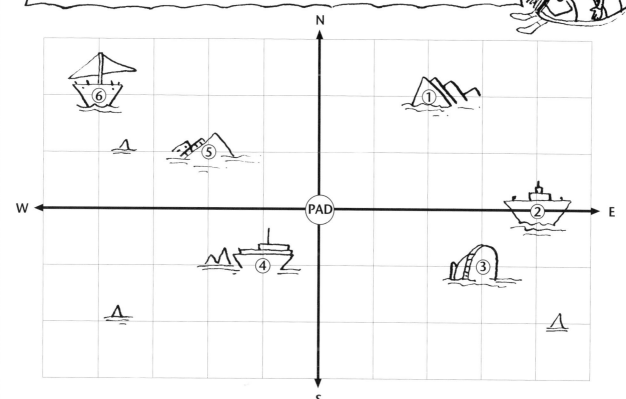

ALERT FORMS

① **Boat in distress at:** an approximate bearing of _____° and a distance of _____ nautical miles.	② **Boat in distress at:** an approximate bearing of _____° and a distance of _____ nautical miles.
③ **Boat in distress at:** an approximate bearing of _____° and a distance of _____ nautical miles.	④ **Boat in distress at:** an approximate bearing of _____° and a distance of _____ nautical miles.
⑤ **Boat in distress at:** an approximate bearing of _____° and a distance of _____ nautical miles.	⑥ **Boat in distress at:** an approximate bearing of _____° and a distance of _____ nautical miles.

NOW TRY THIS!

● A boat is in distress at an approximate bearing of 023° from the helipad, at a distance of 13 nautical miles. The helicopter flies to the boat by travelling due North and then due East.

How far North? _____ How far East? _____

 A **bearing** should always contain three figures. For angles up to 100°, write a zero at the beginning (for example, 054°, 012°, 030°). To find the distance using **Pythagoras' theorem**, remember that the sum of the squares of the two smaller sides of a right-angled triangle is equal to the square of the hypotenuse. This can be written as $c^2 = a^2 + b^2$, where c is the hypotenuse.

Developing Numeracy
Measures, Shape and Space
Year 9
© A & C BLACK

Circumference clues

A

To find the circumference of a circle, you can multiply the diameter by π.
This can be written as:

| Circumference = π × d | or | Circumference = π × r × 2 |

Find the circumference of each circle using the π key. Round your answers to 2 d.p.

(a)
3 cm

C = _18.85 cm_

(b)
5 cm

C = _____

(c)
4 cm

C = _____

(d)
2 cm

C = _____

(e)
6.5 cm

C = _____

(f)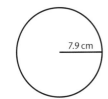
7.9 cm

C = _____

(g)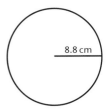
8.8 cm

C = _____

(h)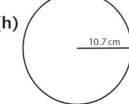
10.7 cm

C = _____

B

1. A wheel rolls through one complete turn along a straight line. The start and finish points are marked with crosses. Find the radius of each wheel to the nearest millimetre. Approximate first.

> The length of the line is equivalent to the circumference of the wheel.

(a)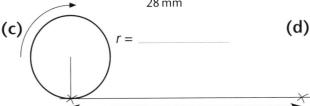
r = _____ mm

28 mm

(b)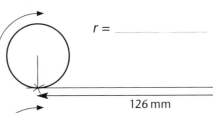
r = _____

367 mm

(c)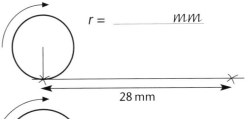
r = _____

440 mm

(d)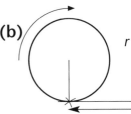
r = _____

126 mm

(e)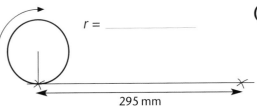
r = _____

295 mm

(f)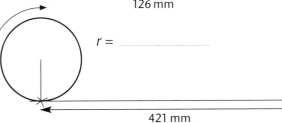
r = _____

421 mm

2. Check your answers by using the radius to find the circumference.

Use the π key on your calculator or take π to be 3.14. To find the radius in part B, you could take the formula C = π × r × 2 and rearrange it to make the formula $r = \frac{C}{2\pi}$.

Developing Numeracy
Measures, Shape and Space
Year 9
© A & C BLACK

Circumference clues

1. A unicycle wheel has a diameter of 60 cm.
How many rotations (to the nearest rotation) will the
wheel make if the unicycle travels in one direction for:

(a) 1696 cm? _____ **(b)** 4500 cm? _____ **(c)** 7351 cm? _____

(d) 330 m? _____ **(e)** 500 m? _____ **(f)** 1 km? _____

2. A jewellery shop sells brooches made from wire. Find the length of
wire used (to 2 d.p.) for these brooches. They are *not* drawn to scale.

(a)

Each diameter is 1.5 cm.

Length of wire: _____

(b)

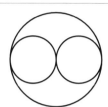

The diameter of the
larger circle is 5 cm.

Length of wire: _____

(c)

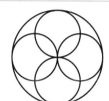

The diameter of the
larger circle is 4 cm.

Length of wire: _____

(d)

This semicircle has
a radius of 3 cm.

Length of wire: _____

(e)

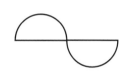

Both semicircles have
a radius of 2.5 cm.

Length of wire: _____

(f)

Each arc is half the circumference
of a circle with a radius of 2.8 cm.

Length of wire: _____

(g)

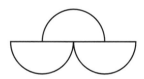

Each semicircle has
a radius of 5 cm.

Length of wire: _____

(h)

This shape is one quarter of a
circle that has a radius of 4 cm.

Length of wire: _____

(i)

Each arc is a quarter of the
circumference of a circle with
a radius of 2 cm.

Length of wire: _____

NOW TRY THIS!

● Find the length of each bold arc.

(a)

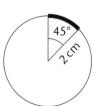

(b)

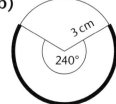

(c)

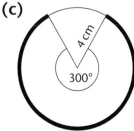

(d)

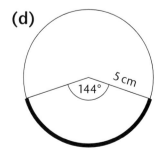

To find the circumference of a circle, use the formula $C = \pi \times d$ or
$C = \pi \times r \times 2$ (where C is the circumference, d is the diameter and r is the
radius). To solve the 'Now try this!' challenge, first find the circumference
of the circle. Then work out what fraction of the circumference each arc is.

Never-ending circles

Special offer

A

The area of a circle is found by squaring the radius and multiplying by π.
This can be written as:

Area of circle = π × r × r   or   Area of circle = πr^2

Circular tin lids of different sizes are cut from sheets of aluminium.

Use the x^2 and the π key to find the area of each tin lid. Round your answers to 2 d.p.

(a)
4.1 cm

Area = _____ cm^2

(b)
6.2 cm

Area = _____

(c)
4.9 cm

Area = _____

(d)
3.7 cm

Area = _____

(e)
5.4 cm

Area = _____

(f)
7.3 cm

Area = _____

(g)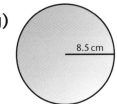
8.5 cm

Area = _____

(h)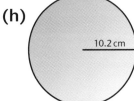
10.2 cm

Area = _____

B

1. A machine cuts 24 circles from a
rectangular sheet of aluminium
measuring 50 cm × 30 cm.
The radius of each circle is 3.7 cm.

30 cm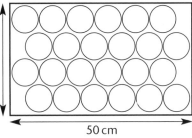

50 cm

(a) What is the area of the aluminium sheet?

_____

(b) What area of aluminium sheeting is wasted
when these circles are cut from the sheet?

_____

2. (a) What is the maximum number of circles, with radius 4.9 cm,

that can be cut from a sheet of the same size? _____

(b) What area of aluminium sheeting is wasted? _____

4.9 cm

See ya—
wouldn't
wanna
be ya!

3. (a) What is the maximum number of circles, with radius 8.5 cm,

that can be cut from a sheet of the same size? _____

(b) What area of aluminium sheeting is wasted? _____

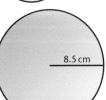
8.5 cm

In part B, you might find it useful to make a scale drawing of the
aluminium sheet, using the scale 1 cm to 10 cm. This can help you to
decide on the maximum number of circles that can be cut.

Find the area
of a circle and
solve problems

C Calculate the area of the shaded parts in each diagram.
Round your answers to 2 d.p.

Use the formula
Area of circle = πr^2.

!

(a)

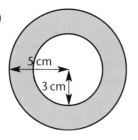

5 cm
3 cm

cm^2

(b)

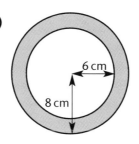

6 cm
8 cm

(c)

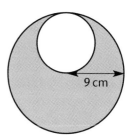

9 cm

(d)

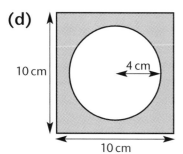

10 cm
4 cm
10 cm

(e)

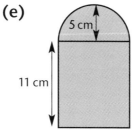

5 cm
11 cm

(f)

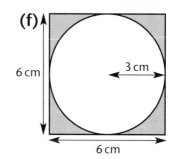

6 cm
3 cm
6 cm

(g)

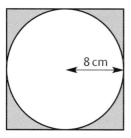

8 cm

(h)

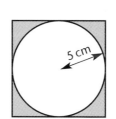

5 cm

(i)

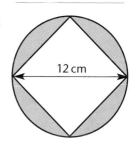

12 cm

(j)

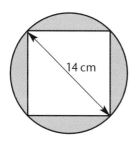

14 cm

(k)

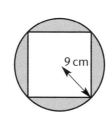

9 cm

(l)

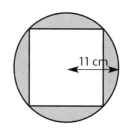

11 cm

**NOW
TRY
THIS!**

- This diagram shows two identical circles overlapping.
  The shaded part is $\frac{1}{4}$ of the area of one circle.
  The area of the whole shape is 77 cm^2.

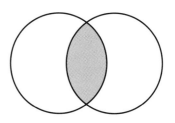

  (a) What is the area of the shaded part? _____

  (b) What is the radius of the circles? _____

To find the area of the shaded parts of a diagram, first find the area of both
the shapes in the diagram: for example, in question (a) find the area of the
large circle and then the small circle. Then subtract the area of the
unshaded part. When you find the area of a circle, use the π key on your
calculator.

At full volume

A Calculate the **volume** of each prism. First find the area of the end-face, then multiply this by its length.

The prisms are not drawn to scale.

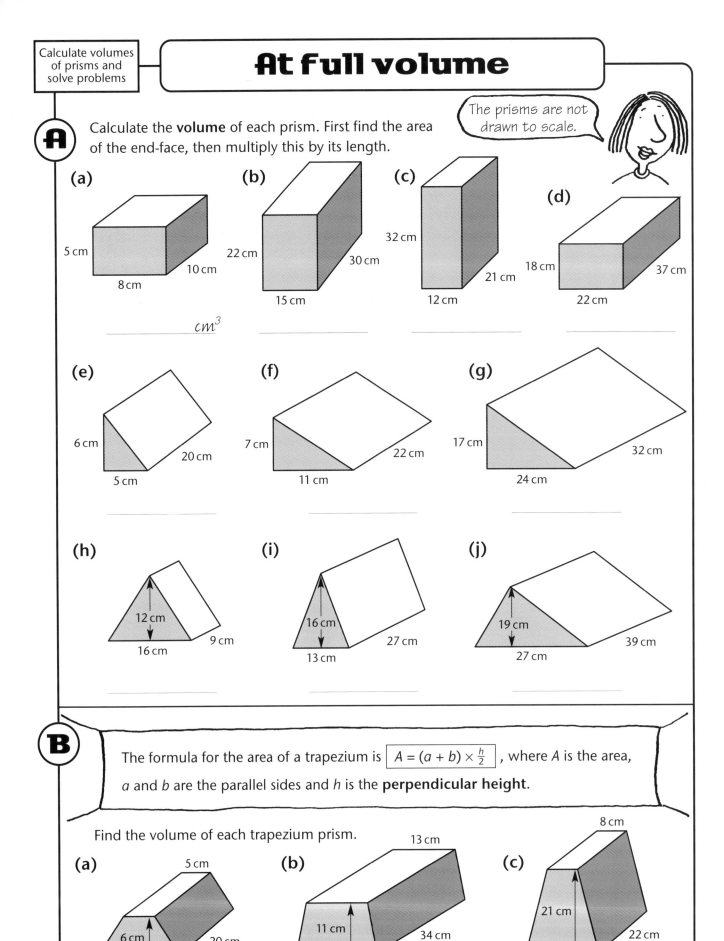

(a) 5 cm, 8 cm, 10 cm

(b) 22 cm, 15 cm, 30 cm

(c) 32 cm, 12 cm, 21 cm

(d) 18 cm, 22 cm, 37 cm

cm^3

(e) 6 cm, 5 cm, 20 cm

(f) 7 cm, 11 cm, 22 cm

(g) 17 cm, 24 cm, 32 cm

(h) 12 cm, 16 cm, 9 cm

(i) 16 cm, 13 cm, 27 cm

(j) 19 cm, 27 cm, 39 cm

B The formula for the area of a trapezium is $\boxed{A = (a + b) \times \frac{h}{2}}$, where A is the area, a and b are the parallel sides and h is the **perpendicular height**.

Find the volume of each trapezium prism.

(a) 5 cm, 6 cm, 20 cm, 13 cm

(b) 13 cm, 11 cm, 34 cm, 17 cm

(c) 8 cm, 21 cm, 22 cm, 19 cm

The **volume** of a 3-D shape is the amount of space it takes up. Volume is measured in cubic centimetres (cm³) or cubic metres (m³). In part B, remember that the area of a prism can be found by multiplying the area of the end-face by the length of the prism. The **perpendicular height** of a trapezium is the distance between the two parallel sides.

Developing Numeracy
Measures, Shape and Space
Year 9
© A & C BLACK

C

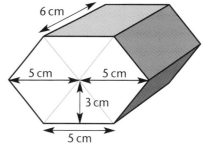

1. The end-face of this prism is a hexagon.
Split it into triangles to help you calculate the
area of the end-face. Then multiply your answer
by the length to find the **volume** of the prism.

Volume = _____

2. Find the volume of these hexagonal prisms in the same way. They are *not* drawn to scale.

(a)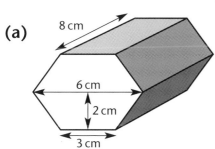

(b)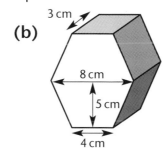

(c)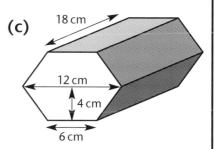

3. Find the volume of each prism. First split the end-face into rectangles or triangles.

(a)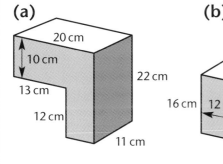

(b)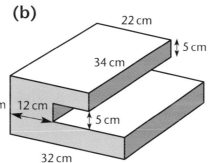

(c)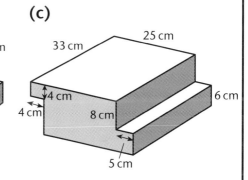

(d)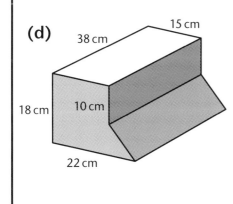

(e)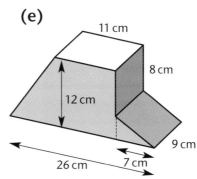

(f)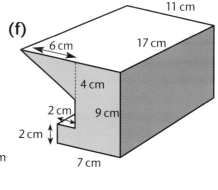

**NOW
TRY
THIS!**

• Imagine you have a box full of small polystyrene balls. The volume of the box is 2400 cm³.
Work out the dimensions of four different prisms that the polystyrene balls would fill
completely. Sketch the prisms and label the dimensions.

The **volume** of a 3-D shape is the amount of space it takes up. Volume is
measured in cubic centimetres (cm³) or cubic metres (m³). Remember:
1 m³ is the same as $100 \times 100 \times 100$ cm³ = 1 000 000 cm³. The diagrams on
this page are not drawn to scale.

A prism sentence

A Sketch the net for each prism. Label the dimensions. Then use your sketches to help you find the **surface area** of each prism.

(a) 3 cm, 8 cm, 7 cm

(b) 5 cm, 9 cm, 6 cm

(c) 11.2 cm, 5 cm, 10 cm, 7 cm

_____ cm^2 _____ _____

(d) 6 cm, 6 cm, 4 cm, 11 cm, 9 cm

(e) 4 cm, 10 cm, 9.8 cm, 8 cm, 8 cm

(f) 11 cm, 4 cm, 4.6 cm

> **!** This hexagon face is **regular**.

_____ _____ _____

B Write dimensions on these prisms so that each has a surface area of between 100 cm² and 120 cm² inclusive. Then find the exact surface area and volume of each.

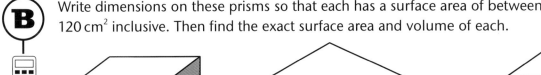

Surface area _____   Surface area _____   Surface area _____

Volume _____   Volume _____   Volume _____

The **surface area** of a 3-D shape is the amount of surface on all its faces added together. It can be found by thinking of each face in turn and finding the area. To find the surface area of a cuboid, you can use the formula **S = 2bl + 2lh + 2hb** (where *l* is length, *b* is breadth and *h* is height). Remember, a **regular** shape has equal sides and equal angles.

Developing Numeracy
Measures, Shape and Space
Year 9
© A & C BLACK

A prism sentence

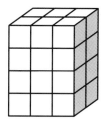

C

1. This cuboid is made from 24 centimetre cubes.
It is lowered into a pot of paint so that the whole
surface area is covered with paint, and left to dry.
The cuboid is then broken into single cubes.

(a) What is the total area of the faces covered with paint? _____

(b) What fraction of all the faces of the cubes is covered with paint? _____

How many of the cubes have:

(c) 0 faces painted? _____   **(d)** 1 face painted? _____   **(e)** 2 faces painted? _____

(f) 3 faces painted? _____   **(g)** more than 3 faces painted? _____

2. Repeat question 1 for a cuboid made from
24 centimetre cubes arranged like this:

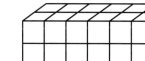

(a) _____

(b) _____

(c) _____   **(d)** _____   **(e)** _____

(f) _____   **(g)** _____

3. Find the **surface area** and volume of each prism.

(a)
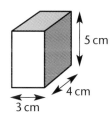
5 cm
4 cm
3 cm

Surface area _____

Volume _____

(b)
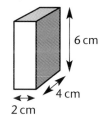
6 cm
4 cm
2 cm

Surface area _____

Volume _____

(c)
5 cm
8 cm
3 cm

Surface area _____

Volume _____

(d)
7 cm   5 cm
4 cm
3 cm

Surface area _____

Volume _____

(e)
4 cm   5.8 cm
3 cm
5 cm

Surface area _____

Volume _____

(f)
9 cm   5.4 cm
5 cm
4 cm

Surface area _____

Volume _____

NOW TRY THIS!

• Write an expression in its simplest form to show the
surface area of this cuboid.

• If its surface area is 52 cm³, find the dimensions of the
cuboid using your expression.

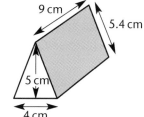
x
$x + 1$
$2x$

 The **surface area** of a 3-D shape is the amount of surface on all its faces
added together. It can be found by thinking of each face in turn and
finding the area. To find the surface area of a cuboid, you can use the
formula **$S = 2bl + 2lh + 2hb$** (where l is length, b is breadth and h is
height).

Developing Numeracy
Measures, Shape and Space
Year 9
© A & C BLACK

59

p 8

B1

Parallel lines:	lines which are equidistant
Rectangle:	a quadrilateral with four right angles
Polygon:	a 2-D closed shape with straight sides
Quadrilateral:	a four-sided polygon
Parallelogram:	a four-sided polygon with two pairs of parallel sides
Rhombus:	a quadrilateral with four equal sides
Hexagon:	a six-sided polygon
Regular polygon:	a polygon with equal sides and equal angles
Square:	a quadrilateral with four equal sides and four right angles

p 9

C Example answers:

(a) Its angles are all equal. Each angle is 60°.
It has 3 lines of reflection symmetry and rotation symmetry of order 3.

(b) Opposite sides are equal and opposite angles are equal.
Adjacent angles total 180°.

(c) All its diagonals are of equal length.
It has the same number of lines of reflection symmetry and order of rotation symmetry as number of sides.

(d) The interior angles of a polygon are measured in degrees.
The amount of turn from one direction to another can be measured in degrees.

(e) The diameter is twice the radius.
Every radius of a circle is the same length.

(f) A perpendicular line segment creates two supplementary angles.
Each supplementary angle is 90°.

p 10

A1 Angles given clockwise from top right:
(a) 60°, 140°, 120°, 40°
(b) 100°, 100°, 120°, 130°, 90°
(c) 85°, 70°, 120°, 85°
(d) 75°, 125°, 105°, 125°, 110°
(e) 100°, 140°, 132°, 92°, 131°, 125°
(f) 120°, 120°, 120°, 120°, 120°, 120°

A2 All 360°

B Angles given clockwise from top right:
(a) Interior: 105°, 90°, 95°, 70°
Exterior: 75°, 90°, 85°, 110°
(b) Interior: 100°, 25°, 125°, 110°
Exterior: 80°, 155°, 55°, 70°
(c) Interior: 56°, 100°, 138°, 104°, 142°
Exterior: 124°, 80°, 42°, 76°, 38°
(d) Interior: 64°, 128°, 89°, 79°
Exterior: 116°, 52°, 91°, 101°
(e) Interior: 94°, 127°, 140°, 109°, 90°, 160°
Exterior: 86°, 53°, 40°, 71°, 90°, 20°
(f) Interior: 110°, 105°, 144°, 108°, 110°, 143°
Exterior: 70°, 75°, 36°, 72°, 70°, 37°

p 11

C2 (a) 90°, 90° (b) 72°, 108° (c) 60°, 120°
(d) 51.4°, 128.6° (e) 45°, 135° (f) 36°, 144°

C3 (a) 12 (b) 15 (c) 18 (d) 36

C4 (a) 15 (b) 12 (c) 16 (d) 20

Now try this!
$180° - (360° \div n)$

p 12

A (a) 360°, 4 sides (b) 540°, 5 sides (c) 360°, 4 sides
(d) 540°, 5 sides (e) 720°, 6 sides (f) 720°, 6 sides

B Angles given clockwise from top right:
(a) 109°, 91°, 93°, 67°
(b) 86°, 49°, 110°, 115°
(c) 109°, 93°, 134°, 68°, 136°
(d) 53°, 122°, 79°, 106°
(e) 112°, 109°, 127°, 129°, 92°, 151°
(f) 111°, 93°, 146°, 108°, 119°, 143°

p 13

C1

Shape	Number of sides	Number of triangles	Number of triangles × 180°	Sum of interior angles
A	4	2	2 × 180°	360°
B	4	2	2 × 180°	360°
C	4	2	2 × 180°	360°
D	5	3	3 × 180°	540°
E	5	3	3 × 180°	540°
F	6	4	4 × 180°	720°
G	6	4	4 × 180°	720°
H	8	6	6 × 180°	1080°
–	n	$n-2$	$(n-2) \times 180°$	$180(n-2)°$

C2 $(n-2) \times 180°$

C3

Shape	Number of sides	Number of triangles	Number of triangles × 180°	Sum of interior angles
P	11	9	9 × 180°	1620°
Q	14	12	12 × 180°	2160°
R	13	11	11 × 180°	1980°
S	28	26	26 × 180°	4680°

Now try this!
$n = 20$

p 14

A a = 109° b = 83° c = 76° d = 104° e = 58°
f = 81° g = 39° h = 111° i = 43° j = 43°
k = 105° l = 110° m = 101° n = 112°
p = 105° q = 122°

B a = 131° b = 99° c = 87°
d = 123° e = 74° f = 74°

p 15

C1 a = 125° b = 55° c = 100°
d = 105° e = 75° f = 50°
g = 55° h = 10° i = 115°
j = 95° k = 20° l = 65°
m = 95° n = 85°
p = 50° q = 130° r = 50°
s = 138° t = 42°

Now try this!
This is true for any quadrilateral with at least one pair of parallel sides: rectangle, rhombus, parallelogram, square and trapezium.

p 16

A2 Isosceles

B (a) L   Acute-angled isosceles
      M   Right-angled isosceles
      N   Equilateral
      O   Acute-angled scalene
      P   Obtuse-angled scalene
      Q   Obtuse-angled isosceles
      R   Right-angled isosceles

    (b) 5

    (c) No, because the sum of the interior angles of a triangle is 180°.

p 17

C1 (a) Rhombus, square
    (b) Parallelogram, rectangle
    (c) Right-angled triangle, trapezium
    (d) Isosceles triangle, trapezium, scalene triangle, right-angled triangle
    (e) Right-angled triangle
    (f) Quadrilateral, kite, isosceles triangle, scalene triangle

C2 (b)

Now try this!
Rectangle:

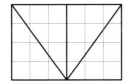

Larger square:

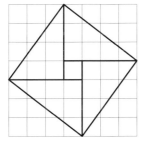

p 18

A1 (a) 3.7 cm, 7 cm, 7.7 cm, 90°, 63°, 27°
      2.9 cm, 4 cm, 4.9 cm, 37°, 53°, 90°
      2.9 cm, 4.4 cm, 5.3 cm, 34°, 56°, 90°
      2.4 cm, 5.9 cm, 6.4 cm, 22°, 68°, 90°
    (b) All are right-angled triangles.
    (c) The right angle.

A2 The smallest angle is opposite the shortest side.

B (a)

Square(s)	Area
A	1 cm²
B	1 cm²
C	2 cm²
A + B	2 cm²
D	4 cm²
E	4 cm²
F	8 cm²
D + E	8 cm²

    (b) The area of the larger square is equal to the total area of the two smaller squares.

p 19

C1 (a) 72 cm²   (b) 89 cm²   (c) 65 cm²
    (d) 80 cm²   (e) 130 cm²   (f) 145 cm²

C2 (a) 10 cm   (b) 11.4 cm   (c) 5 cm
    (d) 13 cm   (e) 12.8 cm   (f) 14.8 cm

Now try this!
10 cm, 24 cm, 26 cm
16 cm, 30 cm, 34 cm

p 20

B (a) False
    (b) True
    (c) True
    (d) False
    (e) True
    (f) False

p 21

C (a) 2 congruent obtuse-angled scalene triangles, 2 congruent acute-angled scalene triangles

    (b) 4 congruent right-angled scalene triangles

    (c) 2 congruent acute-angled scalene triangles, 2 similar obtuse-angled isosceles triangles

    (d) 4 different scalene triangles

    (e) 2 congruent right-angled scalene triangles, 2 different right-angled scalene triangles

    (f) 2 congruent acute-angled isosceles triangles, 2 congruent obtuse-angled isosceles triangles

    (g) 4 congruent right-angled isosceles triangles

Now try this!
Octagon (rotation symmetry of order 4)
Equilateral triangle (rotation symmetry of order 3)
Dodecagon (rotation symmetry of order 6)
Square (rotation symmetry of order 4)

p 22

A (a) circle   (b) arc   (c) radius   (d) circumference
    (e) diameter (f) centre (g) arc   (h) tangent
    (i) semicircle (j) sector (k) chord   (l) segment
    (m) tangent (n) radius (o) segment (p) sector

B (a) tangent   (b) chord   (c) diameter
       1 circle   2 segments   2 semicircles

p 23

Now try this!
2 congruent isosceles triangles

p 24

A (a) 120°   (b) 90°   (c) 72°
    (d) 60°   (e) 51.4° (f) 45°

B (a) 3 isosceles triangles 120°, 30°, 30°
    (b) 4 isosceles triangles 90°, 45°, 45°
    (c) 5 isosceles triangles 72°, 54°, 54°
    (d) 6 equilateral triangles 60°, 60°, 60°
    (e) 7 isosceles triangles 51.4°, 64.3°, 64.3°
    (f) 8 isosceles triangles 45°, 67.5°, 67.5°

p 25

C1 (a) 32.5 cm²   (b) 50 cm²
    (c) 59.4 cm²   (d) 65 cm²
    (e) 68.4 cm²   (f) 70.7 cm²

C2 The sequence of areas (a) to (f) tends towards 78.54 cm² which is the area of the circle.

p 26

A (a) Equilateral triangle, rectangle, rectangle
    (b) Circle, rectangle, rectangle
    (c) Triangle, triangle, square
    (d) Rectangle, rectangle, trapezium

B1 (a) Tetrahedron
    (b) Sphere
    (c) Cuboid
    (d) Hexagonal prism
    (e) Hemisphere
    (f) Octahedron

B2 No

p 28

A1 (a) Square   (b) Square   (c) Rectangle (d) Triangle

A2 (a) Rectangle (b) Equilateral triangle
    (c) Rectangle (d) Rectangle

B1 (a) Square
    (b) A horizontal slice near the apex makes a smaller square; a horizontal slice near the base makes a larger square.

B2 (a) Triangle
    (b) A vertical slice to one side of the apex makes a trapezium or a triangle; a vertical slice through the apex makes a triangle.

p 29

C1 (a) Cube, cube
    (b) Cuboid, cuboid
    (c) Trapezium prism, triangular prism
    (d) Tetrahedron, 7-faced shape
    (e) Triangular prism, triangular prism
    (f) Triangular prism, triangular prism
    (g) Trapezium prism, trapezium prism
    (h) 5-faced shape, 7-faced shape

C2 All six shapes can be made.

Now try this!
The cross-section is always a triangle or a trapezium; the two shapes always have 5 faces.

p 30

A1 (a) Hexagon (b) Heptagon (c) Square   (d) Octagon

A2 (a) Octagon (b) Heptagon (c) Pentagon (d) Octagon

B1 (a) Octagon (b) 16-sided polygon
    (c) Square   (d) 16-sided polygon

B2 (a) 4 right-angled triangles and 4 squares
    (b) 1 octagon, 4 isosceles triangles, 4 right-angled triangles and 8 quadrilaterals
    (c) 1 rhombus, 4 triangles and 2 quadrilaterals
    (d) 4 right-angled kites, 4 quadrilaterals and 8 triangles

p 31

C1 (a) Parallelogram   (b) Rectangle
    (c) Hexagon   (d) Hexagon
    (e) Parallelogram   (f) Parallelogram
    (g) Parallelogram   (h) Hexagon

C2 (a) Yes   (b) No   (c) Yes   (d) Yes
    (e) Yes   (f) Yes   (g) Yes   (h) No

p 32

A (a) True
    (b) True
    (c) False
    (d) True
    (e) True
    (f) False
    (g) False
    (h) False
    (i) True
    (j) False
    (k) True
    (l) False

B1 (a) A rotation clockwise about (2, $^-$5) through 90°.
    (b) A reflection in the line $x = 1$.
    (c) A rotation about (0, $^-$2) through 180°.

B2 (a) Example answer: the translation (0, $^-$7) followed by a reflection in the line $x = 0$ (the y-axis).
    (b) Example answer: the translation (0, 3) followed by a reflection in the line $x = y$.
    (c) Example answer: the translation (0, $^-$1) followed by a reflection in the line $x = 0$.

p 33

C1 (a) K onto L (b) D onto B
    (c) F onto J (d) J onto K
    (e) C onto A (f) I onto E
    (g) L onto J
    (h) G onto E
    (i) F onto C
    (j) H onto G
    (k) E onto B

Now try this!
Reflections and 180° rotations are commutative.

p 34

A1 A, C, D, F, G

A2 3

B1 A, B, D, F

B2 (a) 9
    (b) 7
    (c) An infinite number

p 35

Now try this!
(a) The number of lines of symmetry of end-face + 1
(b) The number of edges of the base face
(c) 9
(d) 10

p 36

A2 (a) 2.4 cm   (b) 4.8 cm
    (c) 2.1 cm   (d) 4.2 cm
    (e) 2.2 cm   (f) 4.4 cm
    (g) 1.4 cm   (h) 2.8 cm

A3 The angles are the same.

A4 Yes

B1 (a) Shapes are similar. Scale factor = 3
    (b) Shapes are similar. Scale factor = 1.5
    (c) Shapes are similar. Scale factor = 5.5
    (d) Shapes are similar. Scale factor = 3.4

p 37

Now try this!
Multiply the perimeter of the original shape by the scale factor.

p 38

A (a) SF 2 (b) SF 4 (c) SF 5
(d) SF 6 (e) SF 8 (f) SF 2
(g) SF 3 (h) SF 4 (i) SF 2

B1 A = 34 mm B = 58 mm C = 136 mm
D = 170 mm E = 204 mm F = 272 mm

B2 (a) SF 2 2
(b) SF 4 4
(c) SF 5 5
(d) SF 6 6
(e) SF 8 8

B3 They are the same.

p 39

C1 (a) 6 cm^2
(b) Area of B 24 cm^2
Area of C 54 cm^2
Area of D 96 cm^2
Area of E 150 cm^2
Area of F 216 cm^2
Area of G 294 cm^2
(c) B 4
C 9
D 16
E 25
F 36
G 49
(d) They are all square numbers. Area increases by the scale factor squared.

C2 (a) 384 cm^2 (b) 600 cm^2 (c) 864 cm^2 (d) 2400 cm^2

Now try this!
5

p 40

A1 1 cm to 1 km —— 1 : 100 000
1 cm to 2 m —— 1 : 200
1 cm to 5 km —— 1 : 500 000
1 cm to 20 m —— 1 : 2000
5 cm to 1 m —— 1 : 20
2 cm to 1 m —— 1 : 50
2 cm to 1 km —— 1 : 50 000

A2 (a) 1 : 1000 (b) 1 : 500
(c) 1 : 500 (d) 1 : 250
(e) 1 : 20 000 (f) 1 : 1 000 000
(g) 1 : 12 (h) 1 : 36

B1 1 cm to 20 m

B2 (a) 80 m (b) 220 m (c) 360 m
(d) 380 m (e) 500 m (f) 580 m

B3 (a) 0.5 cm (b) 2 cm (c) 5 cm
(d) 3.5 cm (e) 11.5 cm (f) 50 cm

p 41

C1

	Scaled length	Actual length
a	6 cm	9 m
b	4 cm	6 m
c	12 cm	18 m
d	8 cm	12 m
e	3 cm	4.5 m
f	2.5 cm	3.75 m
g	2 cm	3 m
h	0.5 cm	0.75 m
i	1.6 cm	2.4 m
j	1.2 cm	1.8 m

C2 Scaled area = 5 cm^2
Actual area = 11.25 m^2 or 112 500 cm^2
No, it is 22 500 times larger (150 × 150).

Now try this!
a = 7.2 cm b = 4.8 cm c = 14.4 cm d = 9.6 cm e = 3.6 cm
f = 3 cm g = 2.4 cm h = 0.6 cm i = 1.92 cm j = 1.44 cm

p 42

A1 AB (2, 4)
CD ($^-$7, 3)
EF ($^-$3, 3)
GH (5, $^-$1)
KL ($^-$2, $^-$4)

B1 (a) ($^-$0.5, $^-$1) (b) (1, 0) (c) ($^-$0.5, $^-$3)
(d) ($^-$4, 1) (e) ($^-$2, $^-$1) (f) (3, 2)
(g) (4, $^-$5) (h) (1, $^-$5) (i) (1, $^-$2)

p 43

C1 AB = 5.8 units
CD = 6.7 units
EF = 7.8 units
GH = 15.8 units

Now try this!
$d = \sqrt{[(x_1 - x_2)^2 + (y_1 - y_2)^2]}$

p 44

B2 (a) 6.2 cm (b) 4 cm
(c) 5.7 cm (d) 8.8 cm (e) 12 cm

p 45

C1 (a) 11.3 m (b) 10.6 m
(c) 9.5 m (d) 9.7 m
(e) 11.8 m (f) 8.6 m
(g) 7.6 m (h) 12.5 m

Now try this!
Ladders (a), (c) and (g) are unsafe.

p 46

A1 (a) Circle
(b) A line perpendicular to a straight line joining the two bulls
(c) Two lines and two semicircles joined around the bench
(d) Sphere

B2 19.2 m^2

p 47

C1 A

C2 C

C3 Rectangle → cylinder
Triangle → cone
Pentagon → cylinder
Trapezium → truncated cone

Now try this!
The fly can be on any of the three adjacent faces, on the arcs shown.

Front face Side face Top face

p 48

A2 (a) 500 mm²   (b) 1200 mm²
(c) 500 cm²   (d) 750 cm²
(e) 60 000 cm²   (f) 150 000 cm²
(g) 6.5 m²   (h) 15 m²

A3 (a) 5 ha   (b) 12.5 ha   (c) 0.5 ha
(d) 10 ha   (e) 35 ha   (f) 0.25 ha

B2 (a) 4000 mm³   (b) 10 000 mm³
(c) 50 cm³   (d) 28 cm³
(e) 100 000 000 cm³   (f) 1 000 000 000 cm³
(g) 2 m³   (h) 0.5 m³

p 49

C1 (a) 2100 mm²   (b) 6400 mm²
(c) 3200 mm²   (d) 4000 mm²

C2 (a) 560 000 mm³   (b) 72 000 mm³   (c) 224 000 mm³
(d) 269 500 mm³   (e) 162 000 mm³   (f) 17 864 mm³

Now try this!
(a) 44 400 mm²   (b) 10 800 mm²   (c) 23 200 mm²
(d) 28 000 mm²   (e) 18 450 mm²   (f) 4132 mm²

p 50

A1 (a) 210°
(b) 150°
(c) 030°

A2 (a) 290°
(b) 070°
(c) 110°

A3 (a) 240°
(b) 120°
(c) 060°

A4 (a) 260°
(b) 100°
(c) 080°

B1 (a) 045°
(b) 255°
(c) 355°
(d) 135°
(e) 225°
(f) 317°

p 51

C Bearings are approximate.
Boat 1: 045°   2.8 nautical miles
Boat 2: 090°   4 nautical miles
Boat 3: 108°   3.2 nautical miles
Boat 4: 225°   1.4 nautical miles
Boat 5: 297°   2.25 nautical miles
Boat 6: 297°   4.5 nautical miles

Now try this!
12 nautical miles North, 5 nautical miles East

p 52

A (a) 18.85 cm   (b) 31.42 cm   (c) 25.13 cm   (d) 12.57 cm
(e) 40.84 cm   (f) 49.64 cm   (g) 55.29 cm   (h) 67.23 cm

B1 (a) 4 mm   (b) 58 mm
(c) 70 mm   (d) 20 mm
(e) 47 mm   (f) 67 mm

p 53

C1 (a) 9   (b) 24   (c) 39
(d) 175   (e) 265   (f) 531

C2 (a) 14.14 cm   (b) 31.42 cm   (c) 37.70 cm
(d) 15.42 cm   (e) 25.70 cm   (f) 35.19 cm
(g) 67.12 cm   (h) 14.28 cm   (i) 22.57 cm

Now try this!
(a) 1.57 cm   (b) 12.57 cm   (c) 20.94 cm   (d) 12.57 cm

p 54

A (a) 52.81 cm²   (b) 120.76 cm²
(c) 75.43 cm²   (d) 43.01 cm²
(e) 91.61 cm²   (f) 167.42 cm²
(g) 226.98 cm²   (h) 326.85 cm²

B1 (a) 1500 cm²
(b) 467.8 cm²

B2 (a) 15
(b) 368.5 cm²

B3 (a) 3
(b) 819.1 cm²

p 55

C Answers using π key on calculator:
(a) 50.27 cm²   (b) 87.96 cm²   (c) 190.85 cm²
(d) 49.73 cm²   (e) 149.3 cm²   (f) 7.73 cm²
(g) 54.94 cm²   (h) 21.46 cm²   (i) 41.10 cm²
(j) 55.94 cm²   (k) 92.47 cm²   (l) 138.13 cm²

Now try this!
(a) 11 cm²   (b) 3.74 cm

p 56

A (a) 400 cm³   (b) 9900 cm³
(c) 8064 cm³   (d) 14 652 cm³
(e) 300 cm³   (f) 847 cm³   (g) 6528 cm³
(h) 864 cm³   (i) 2808 cm³   (j) 10 003.5 cm³

B (a) 1080 cm³   (b) 5610 cm³   (c) 6237 cm³

p 57

C1 270 cm³

C2 (a) 144 cm³   (b) 180 cm³   (c) 1296 cm³

C3 (a) 3124 cm³   (b) 12 308 cm³   (c) 11 220 cm³
(d) 11 324 cm³   (e) 1614 cm³   (f) 1037 cm³

p 58

A (a) 202 cm²   (b) 258 cm²   (c) 371 cm²
(d) 267 cm²   (e) 459.2 cm²   (f) 358.8 cm²

p 59

C1 (a) 52 cm²
(b) $\frac{13}{36}$
(c) 0   (d) 4   (e) 12
(f) 8   (g) 0

C2 (a) 56 cm²
(b) $\frac{7}{18}$
(c) 0   (d) 0   (e) 16
(f) 8   (g) 0

C3 (a) 94 cm²
     60 cm³
(b) 88 cm²
     48 cm³
(c) 158 cm²
     120 cm³
(d) 96 cm²
     42 cm³
(e) 70.2 cm²
     30 cm³
(f) 165.8 cm²
     90 cm³

Now try this!
Surface area = $10x^2 + 6x$
If surface area is 52 cm³, $x = 2$
Dimensions are 2 cm, 3 cm, 4 cm

64